Elkins (ed.)
Visual Practices Across the University

Visual Practices Across the University

Edited by James Elkins

Wilhelm Fink Verlag

This book was kindly supported by the School of the Art Institute of Chicago, U.S.A.

Bibliografische Information der Deutschen Nationalbibliothek

Die Deutsche Nationalbibliothek verzeichnet diese Publikation in der Deutschen Nationalbibliografie; detaillierte bibliografische Daten sind im Internet über http://dnb.d-nb.de abrufbar.

© 2007 Wilhelm Fink Verlag, München
(Wilhelm Fink GmbH & Co. Verlags-KG, Jühenplatz 1, D-33098 Paderborn)

Internet: www.fink.de

Einbandgestaltung: Evelyn Ziegler, München
Herstellung: Ferdinand Schöningh GmbH & Co. KG, Paderborn

ISBN 978-3-7705-4373-1

Table of Contents

image-making takes place in a wide range of disciplines

Preface

This is an experimental book. It is an attempt to think about images beyond the familiar confines of fine art, and even beyond the broadening interests of the new field of visual studies. Outside of painting, sculpture, and architecture, and outside of television, advertising, film, and other mass media, what kinds of images do people care about? It turns out that images are being made and discussed in dozens of fields, throughout the university and well beyond the humanities. Some fields, such as biochemistry and astronomy, are image-obsessed; others think and work *through* images.

So far visual studies has mainly taken an interest in fine art and mass media, leaving these other images — which are really the vast majority of all images produced in universities — relatively unstudied. Outside the university, scientific images crop up in magazines, on the internet, in popular-science books, and in the familiar "art meets science" exhibitions. In those contexts images are often drastically simplified, shorn of much of the significance they had for their makers. Here I try to pay close-grained attention to the ways people make and talk about images in some thirty fields across all the faculties of a typical contemporary university. There are examples in these pages of the study of dolphins' fins, of porcelain teeth, of Cheddar cheese. I am less interested in what might count as art or science, or in what might be of interest from an aesthetic (or anti-aesthetic) point of view, than I am in simply *listening* to the exact and often technical ways in which images are discussed.

A great deal is at stake on this apparently unpromising ground. It is widely acknowledged that ours is an increasingly visual society, and yet the fields that want to provide the theory of that visuality — visual studies, art history, philosophy, sociology — continue to take their examples from the tiny minority of images that figure as art. At the same time, there is an increasingly reflective and complicated discourse on the nature of universities, which has as one of its tropes the notion that the university is "in ruins" or is otherwise fragmented. One way to bring it together, or at least to raise the possibility that the university is a coherent place, is to consider different disciplines through their visual practices. To begin a university-wide discussion of images, it is first necessary to stop worrying about what might count as art or science, and to think instead about how kinds of image-making and image interpretation might fall into groups, and therefore be amenable to teaching and learning outside their disciplines. Above all, it is necessary to look carefully and in detail, and not flinch from technical language or even from the odd equation.

All these points are theorized in the Introduction, but the book can also be read by browsing the chapters and picking up the themes as they occur. If you encounter them singly, the chapters may seem fixated on facts and procedures,

My dissertation aims at articulating the "particulate detail" of an unusual visual practice.

and short on connections. This is intentional and important. <u>Large-scale, generalized notions of images and visuality weigh down visual studies.</u> (Even those few scholars who *do* look at images outside of art tend to theorize them all together, substituting general theories of images for general theories of images in art.) If we are to move beyond that critical inertia, then we need to let individual image-making practices exist in all their splendid particulate detail. There are five large and several smaller themes threaded through this book, and some large-scale claims about the place of visuality in the humanities and in the university (all are set out in the Introduction); but I have tried not to let any one discourse subsume the quirkiness and texture of real practices. It is crucial, I think, to resist the desire to create continuous narratives out of specific practices, to decline the temptation to soften jargon, to refuse — at least temporarily — to assign meaning to apparently inarticulate computational practices. Those desires are typical of the humanities when they look to the sciences. Hence the particulate, sometimes rebarbative nature of this book: it is an experiment in mingling the humanities' passion for image theory with the many modest and local practices that constitute image-making throughout the university.

There isn't any easy way to acknowledge the people who helped with this book. Each chapter has been extensively rewritten in collaboration with the authors, in some cases as many as fifteen times, and sometimes from scratch. Each chapter also existed as wall text in the original exhibition in 2005, and over half the authors also wrote PowerPoint presentations and gave lectures to a class I supervised on the subject the following year. Twenty other proposals did not go into either the exhibition or the book, two others were in the class but not the book; and about twenty outside specialists were consulted on various points. (Special thanks to Aileen Dillane, Áine Hyland, and Frank van Pelt, who gave lectures in the class but were not in the book or the exhibition.) Some authors worked on numerous revisions from summer 2003 up to the exhibition in April 2005, to the class in winter 2006, and on to the book in May 2006.

So: a massive amount of work was involved for everyone, involving many times the page count of this book, and I am tremendously grateful. I also want to acknowledge the staff of the Lewis Glucksman Gallery at University College, Cork, and in particular Fiona Kearney, the Gallery's enthusiastic and committed Director; René Zechlin, an innovative curator who had the unenviable task of printing the almost 25,000 words of text that went onto the walls at the exhibit; my colleague Sabine Kriebel; and many others, especially Nora Hickey, the very skilful James Cronin, and Veronica Fraser, the truly remarkable Department secretary who not only managed everything connected with these events, but read the texts and participated in the reading groups. Finally, special thanks to Gerard Wrixon, then President of the University, who was directly responsible for the development of arts, the Gallery, and the new Department of the History of Art.

Introduction

This book began with an exhibition of the same name, held in Cork, Ireland, in 2005. The exhibition was originally intended to be published along with a conference called "Visual Literacy," in a single large book. In fact the conference will appear as two separate books.[1] (More on that in the Afterword.)

For the exhibition, I sent an email inquiry to all the faculty in the sixty-odd departments at University College Cork, asking for proposals from anyone who used images in their work. The initial responses developed into thirty displays; each was accompanied by up to a thousand words of wall text. The exhibition represented all the faculties of the university, from Arts to Medicine, Food Science to Law. It only had a couple of displays of fine art: one proposed by a colleague in History of Art, and another by a scholar in the History Department. Fine art was swamped, as I had hoped it would be, by the wide range of image-making throughout the university. This book is a rethought and rearranged version of the wall texts in the original exhibition; each one has been rewritten and expanded, to bring out themes that emerged during and after the exhibition.

This Introduction is divided into four parts. First, some distinctions between what is done here, and what happens in exhibitions and books that present science as art or look for the art in science. Then a sketch of how images might be understood when the art-science distinction is not the crucial one. Third, a review of the principal themes that emerged in the course of the exhibition, which I have tried to bring out in the book; and fourth, the possibility that this kind of material might be used in a university-wide introductory course on visual practices.

Attempts to present science as art, and vice versa

Among the things that this book is not, it is primarily not a contribution to the many exhibitions and books that present scientific images as art, or as possessing the aesthetic properties or even the "richness" that supposedly inhere in art. In this book I will be ignoring the intermittent temptation to say such-and-such an image is beautiful, and I will not be presenting any image, no matter how luscious, as possessing any aesthetic properties that its maker or its intended audience have not already claimed for it. My interest is the particular ways of talking about images in different fields. (It happens that some ways of talking about images incorporate the kinds of broad claims about art or science that I want to avoid, and it often happens that people call one another's images "beautiful," but reporting on other people's use of such claims is different from using them to organize the argument.)

The most widely publicized recent conferences on science-art themes are Felice Frankel's two "Image and Meaning Initiative" conferences, the first at MIT in June 2001, and the second at the Getty Center in Los Angeles in June 2005.[2]

Frankel is a science photographer, originally trained as a landscape and garden photographer, who rephotographs scientific experiments for publication.[3] In the past her work has raised interesting questions about the relation between her artistic choices and the scientists' visual preferences, especially when her rephotographs have helped scientists discover new features of their work that they had not seen.[4] Her books *On the Surface of Things* and *Envisioning Science: The Design and Craft of the Science Image* present accomplished, colorful photographs of various physical and chemical phenomena. Frankel's conferences and books provide a chance for art photographers to think about scientific images, and for scientists to ponder such things as the place of beauty or art in visualization. Phenomena such as iridescence on an oil surface, colors generated by opal, and patterns of crystals on a surface, are visualized in great detail and with attention to composition and symmetry. The photographs' formal properties are, however, untheorized. Frankel presents her work as "scientific photography" and writes only as a technical photographer. She does not articulate the artistic influences on her own work, even though that history is pertinent because it guides her choices of compositions, colors, symmetries, and textures. Frankel's books therefore lack the analysis of artistic influences that might have been able to account for her photographic preferences. Her compositional choices, for example, are influenced — I assume mostly indirectly, without deliberation — by Abstract Expressionism, and by realist projects such as the Boyle Family's fiberglass castings. In art historical terms, her practice derives from several strands of modern painting and photography from the 1940s to the 1980s. Those precedents are not irrelevant, because they can illuminate the aesthetic decisions that appear, unexplained, simply as "beauty." And because she does not know the science except to the extent that it is explained to her, the scientific content of her images is seldom broached except in the most general terms. For the book *On the Surface of Things,* a prominent chemist provided very brief, nontechnical summaries of the relevant science — not enough to account for individual passages in Frankel's very complex and detailed images. As a result Frankel's projects miss the many specific connections between photographic decisions informed by the history of art, on the one hand, and by the scientists' purposes, on the other. Her photographs can only appear as mute testimony to her "eye," her unarticulated judgment of what counts as an interesting image. *On the Surface of Things* is a brilliant coffee-table book: it can be read by scientists and artists; both will recognize meanings that are not spelled out, but neither will know how to make a bridge between the two domains. What is needed, I think, is an inch-by-inch analysis of her photographs, to bring out the individual artistic decisions and their histories, together with — matched line by line with — an inch-by-inch account of the scientific meaning of each form.

Frankel also writes a column called "Sightings" in *American Scientist* magazine, interviewing scientists about their images. One column is an interview with

Jeff Hester of Arizona State University, who was one of the scientists who made the widely-reproduced Hubble Space Telescope image of young stars in the Eagle Nebula (1995).

The interview is brief, only a few paragraphs; and because of its brevity, it is a good example of what I think of as the abbreviated, impoverished structure of much art-science discourse. Hester describes how the image was combined from thirty-two images taken by four separate cameras, and how the images were stitched together, cleaned up, and given false colors. Blue, for example, stands for emissions from doubly ionized oxygen. The colors appear "representational," in Frankel's phrase — that is, they make it seem the photograph is a picture of mountains. Hester explains the image is more like a "map of the physical proper-ties of the gas," but that, fortuitously, "it is also closer to what you might see through a telescope with your eye than is a picture taken with color film."[5] Toward the end of the one-page interview, Hester says "the beauty of the image is not happenstance. When people talk about 'beauty,' they are talking about the presence of pattern in the midst of complexity." Several things need to be asked about that claim if it is to make sense. It would be good to know why Hester felt he should mention beauty at all; I assume it was on account of the popular-science context of the interview, and the idea that beauty might serve as a bridge to a wider public. But what kind of bridge is beauty here? Instead of bringing beauty in, why not present the image as something wonderfully and unexpectedly complex — that is, after all, another alleged art-world value — by saying, as he had a moment before, that "there is one hell of a lot of information present"? And having mentioned beauty, why identify it with pattern recognition? That is not an association I think many people in art would have, unless they are following psychologists such as Rudolph Arnheim.

There are at least five assumptions at work in Hester's mention of beauty, and in Frankel's silence about it: that beauty is relevant, that the image is beautiful, that the meaning of beauty is clear, that beauty can help the image communicate to non-scientists, that beauty is an idea shared across the arts and sciences. Hester remarks that "the same patterns present in the image that make it aesthetically pleasing also make it scientifically interesting." If that were true — and to assent I would have to agree that beauty is present, and that beauty can be identified with pattern recognition — then it would have to mean something like this: If I appreciate the patterns in this image, I also appreciate the science. I think that is untrue, and it is not supported by what Hester says. He concludes that he and his collaborators "use color in the image in much the same way that an artist uses color," as an "interpretive tool." That may mean that the false colors he and his collaborators chose to represent emissions of oxygen, hydrogen, and sulfur are like the false colors artists chose, and it might also mean that artists also choose false colors that are at the same time like representational colors. Either way the parallel is too loose to do much work, and that is one of the reasons conversations like these are often so short.

An artist like Emil Nolde, who chose "false" colors as well as naturalistic ones, made his decisions for completely different reasons — and even using a different palette — than physicists who make false-color astronomical images. Scientists' choice of colors have specific histories, just as artists' choices. Some of the more garish productions of astronomical images owe their color choices to 1960s hallucigenic art like *Yellow Submarine* or tie-dyed T-shirts. The Eagle Nebula image owes its color choices to the history of landscape painting and photography. It has a saturated, Kodachrome look that derives from nostalgic reworkings of 1950s photography, and it also owes something to the kitsch paintings popular in "starving artist" sales and exemplified for North American consumers by the painter Thomas Kinkade. (He paints tumble-down English-style thatched cottages, decorated with rainbow-colored flowers.[6]) In terms of forms, the Eagle

Nebula image as it is presented here (it could have been cropped and oriented quite differently) belongs to the history of romantic landscape painting, from Arnold Böcklin and other German and French painters to the exaggerated mountains of the Hudson River School painters. It may even belong to the lineage of fantastical mountainscapes in Chinese painting, beginning in the Song Dynasty and continuing to the present. I do not mean any of this as a put-down: I want to say scientific images have their own lineages in the history of art, their own aesthetic histories. They are not merely or simply "beautiful" — and "pattern" has little to do with these historical lineages.

And even if artists were to agree that they use false and yet "representational" color "in much the same way," it would still be unclear what about the science has been explained aside from the fact that the colors were chosen to aid communication. Frankel's column does not explain how the image was generated, except in generalities; it does not explain the link that is proposed between art and science; and it does not explain the scientific content of the image. She asks no follow-up questions to Hester's opinions about beauty, art, and pattern.

Hester's brief comments are made in an informal context, but they follow a logic that can be found in many other places.[7] Examples could be multiplied indefinitely. In 2005 an article in *California Monthly,* Berkeley's alumni magazine, showcased the research of Berkeley scientists. In this kind of article, a "pretty picture" (the term was apparently adopted by astronomers to denote images they prepared for calendars and posters) is briefly glossed by a text identifying the scholar who produced it. A full-page photograph of a moss-covered tree, for example, is accompanied by a text describing a Berkeley scientist who recovered medicines from moss, especially "a family of chemicals called flavenoids" (see the illustration on the next page).

Nothing more is said. In the context of an alumni magazine, all that is expected is a nice picture and a reference, and it would be assumed that anyone who wanted could follow up and find out more. But these clipped contexts are ubiquitous, and so it is significant that the text explains neither the photograph (What kind of tree? What kind of moss? Was the picture used in the research?) nor the science (What are flavenoids? How are they extracted?). A reader perusing the article is treated to several dozen photographs and short paragraphs. If they are interested, they can learn the names of the Berkeley scientists and guess at what they are doing, but the article is not really meant to teach anything. It is a wash of colorful images and new names, which suggests that lovely photographs can help lay people understand a little science.

In a lecture given in spring 2005 as part of the Einstein centenary, the physicist Michael Berry of Bristol University visited Ireland and gave a talk about the patterns of light that form on the bottom of swimming pools and the ceilings above swimming pools. The "caustics" and wave fronts were the object of his

Working moss

The Integrative Biology department fosters
cross-disciplinary research. Eric Harris,
a Ph.D. candidate, is studying both the human
use of moss (by Chinese healers) and the
evolutionary history of medicinal mosses.
The active ingredient in *Shui Mu Cao*,
used to treat wounds, is probably a family
of chemicals called flavonoids. Looking
backward, Harris is trying to see what
evolutionary edge these chemicals gave
their mossy hosts. The University and
Jepson Herbaria are joining hands with
the department to support this work.

Epiphytic ferns and mosses on a tree in Yunnan
Province, China. Photo by Eric Harris.

own scientific research, he said, and he also talked about the motion of wave
packets and the physics of rainbows. He compared those phenomena to David
Hockney's paintings, and to passages about reflections and light patterns in A.S.

Byatt, Thomas Pynchon, and John Banville. The occasion was a "Café scienti-
fique" sponsored in part by the British Council, and in that setting it would not
be appropriate to introduce much scientific content. Berry worked on the assumption that the audience found the images as beautiful as he did (I found them
garish), and the theme throughout was that an appreciation of the beauty would
provide a way to appreciate the science. The audience was appreciative because
he talked in a persuasive and animated way and because the images were full of
color and light, but both the science and the art (I mean the Hockney) were done
a disservice. Nothing could be gleaned about the physics of caustics from Berry's
images, and his impoverished sense of artistic beauty made the parallels between
artists like Hockney and the high-chroma scientific photographs unconvinc-
ing.

  In the art world, the same strategies of juxtaposing art and science, and implying that one seeps naturally into the other, produce work that can be taken
tongue-in-cheek, as kitsch. An example at the margins of the art world is the
company DNA 11, which will make framed pictures of your DNA.[8] Although
their website simply identifies the images as DNA — and as "great art," and
"one-of-a-kind masterpieces" — actually they are electrophoretograms, arranged
in strips. They are unlabeled, making it virtually impossible to extract any scientific content from them. "The procedure we use," they write, allaying the possible objection that someone could extract information from their "art," "creates
a unique fingerprint that does not provide any information about your genetic
code. It is a unique, artistic representation of your genetic fingerprint." Their art
is beholden to a popularized aesthetic derived from minimalism: the color
schemes they offer, and the frames that consumers can choose, all derive from
second-generation minimalism in the 1990s. Their project can also be taken as just
fun — which is to say as campy pseudo-science, or even kitschy sciencey minimalism. DNA 11's art credentials include the fact that it is advertised specifically
as having no content: you can't learn about your DNA from your DNA art.

  "Beauty" and "art" do not have much analytic purchase in any of these in-
stances. Is Berry's use of the word "beauty", or Hester's use, that different from
Ed Bell's praise of the computer graphics company Hybrid Medical Animation,
when he says their animations "extend beyond the boundary of highly informa-
tive graphics: they enter the realm of high art, achieving a combination of Truth
and Beauty"? Hybrid Medical Animations makes Hollywood-style digital movies of proteins, antibodies, bacteriophages, and other microscopic phenomena
(see the picture on the next page).

  They use the latest textures (translucent surfaces, shining and viscous surfaces), vivid colors (magentas, lavenders) and all the bells and whistles of *Star
Wars*-style action (tracking shots, zooms, fly-throughs, rapid point-of-view
changes, simulated shallow focus). Their movies are like *Star Wars* (or, more
recently, *Starship Troopers*) or a Universal Studios theme park ride, but with

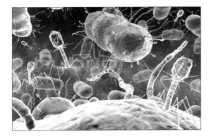 molecules instead of actors. Bell is Art Director of *Scientific American;* his endorsement appears on Hybrid Medical Animation's web pages. "Beauty" would seem to mean something like "dazzling post-production-style visual effects" — different, I think, from Berry's "beautiful" which means something like "elegant curvilinear patterns not unlike Op Art," and from Hester's "beautiful" which means something like "patterns that can be universally recognized."

There is a longer history of displaying scientific images for their beauty. André Kertesz composed scientific images that way, but the most influential example was the philosopher Jean-François Lyotard's exhibition *Les Immatériaux,* which displayed bubble-chamber images as if they were analogues of gestural painters such as Cy Twombly or Antoní Tapies. Bubble chamber images are actually intended to be *measured* and then discarded — more on this later — and not appreciated for any aesthetic property. The exhibition, "Visual Practices Across the University," was intended to break with the tradition of Kertesz and Lyotard and the many people who follow in their wake. In this book, each chapter gets a single large image, as it was in the exhibition: these are lures, and in the exhibition they were meant to give the impression that beauty might be important after all. Visitors were meant to be attracted by the large, unusual images, the way a reader of *California Monthly* might be attracted by the pictures of outer space, molecules, and mossy trees. Then when the visitors approached more closely, they found that the pictures only *appeared* to be accessible, and what little they shared with art — their compositions, their colors — wasn't helpful or interesting.

So one reason to try to stop paying attention to the art-science difference is the impoverished discourse that is built on words like "beauty," "elegance," and "pattern." The opposite also happens: scientists write about artworks as if art's main interest is its scientific content. Thomas Rossing and Christopher Chiaverina's *Light Science: Physics and the Visual Arts,* which finds scientific themes in pointillism, anamorphosis, and op art, is an example: it argues that a principal source of interest in the art is its illustration of basic scientific concepts.[9] Leonard Shlain's *Art and Physics: Parallel Visions in Space, Time, and Light* is a more concerted effort to find links between science and art, but Shlain is too easily satisfied by chance coincidences, metaphoric connections, and miscellaneous affinities.[10] The same could be said of other books, including John Latham's *Art After Physics* and Arturo Gilardoni's *X-Rays in Art.*[11] The common ground of these books is a dual claim: first, that art can be interesting because it demonstrates science; second, that it is not incumbent on someone writing about the science in art to account for the apparent irrelevance of the existing non-scientific interpretations of the art.[12]

A large critical and journalistic literature rose in the wake of a book by David Hockney and Charles Falco called *Secret Knowledge: Rediscovering the Lost Techniques of the Old Masters,* which claims that some old masters used mirrors and other optical devices to help them make naturalistic paintings. There was an enormous conference on the theme in December 2001 at New York University, and several of the people involved continued to publish on the subject in the years following. (My criterion of an enormous conference is that 90 seats were set aside just for journalists, and lines went halfway around Washington Square in Manhattan.) Essentially Hockney and Falco claimed that painters from Van Eyck onward had access to optical aids such as mirrors, camera lucidas, and lenses that helped them achieve the feats of naturalism that have been traditionally attributed to their innate skill. The book and conference were a sensation in the media, in part because they seemed to empower ordinary viewers — at last, so it was said, viewers do not have to listen to the increasingly arcane meditations of academics, because they can see for themselves how the paintings were made.[13]

Ellen Winner, a psychologist who gave a paper at the conference, later wrote an essay called "Art History Can Trade Insights With the Sciences," calling for a mutual respect that she felt was missing at the conference. "True," she writes, "Falco and Hockney did not speak to the meaning or beauty" of the art, but that does not imply there are no lessons to be learned by considering the science. "When art historians argue that artists did not *need* lenses because they were so talented, they seem not to realize that the argument does not rule out the use of lenses."[14] The gulf of misunderstandings I have been trying to describe is nicely contained in that sentence, because regardless of the truth of Hockney's clam, it is not true that "art historians argue that artists did not *need* lenses": they don't argue about those things at all. The two discourses are much further apart than Winner's claim implies, and it is not likely that more than a half-dozen humanists and cognitive scientists are "going to be teaming up to study humanistic phenomena from a scientific perspective." In order for that to happen, there has first to be an agreement over the common problems, whether they are beauty or optics.

Sidney Perkowitz, another scientist who attended the conference on Hockney's book, had written a book called *Empire of Light* (1996). In the article he later contributed to the conference papers, he says he is neither surprised nor dismayed that some artists used optical aids. "Should the use of a tool diminish the value of the art?" he asks, and he illustrates a painting by Chardin, an Op-Art abstraction, and Mondrian's *Broadway Boogie-Woogie.*[15] The question isn't wrong, but wrongheaded. To whom does it matter that Chardin or Mondrian "reflect principles of visual cognition"? That has seldom been a part of their significance, and if the idea is to find examples of visual cognition, there is no good reason to adduce art to begin with. At the conference I had a brief argument with Perkowitz. I suggested that very few contemporary artists even use science in their work — I named Vija Celmins, Dorothea Rockburne, and Mark Tansey — and he said I was wrong, that his book had many examples of "new forms of art" produced by the use of science. His essay features an artist named Dale Edlred (I had not heard of him), and his book has many more minor artists. I wonder if their marginality in the art world does not prove the point. Art that is strongly inclined to technology or science often — though not always — ends up on the margins of the art world. The large annual conferences of SIGGRAPH and ISEA are cases in point; both organizations feature digital art, and both are almost completely ignored by the mainstream art world. In some measure that is a prejudice, and a fault, of the art world: but in some measure it shows that scientific and technological themes just aren't part of the mainstreams of postmodernism.[16]

The principal humanist scholars who study the science of art, such as Martin Kemp and John Gage, have done much of what can be done on the scattered appearances of scientific content in Western art.[17] The end point of such research is the fact that science has rarely constituted much of what matters in art. The complementary end point of the scientific interest in art, such as Thomas Rossing and Christopher Chiaverina's, or Leonard Shlain's, should be that scientific explanations rarely matter in humanist discourse on art. If discourse on science-art connections is rum, uninformed, unhelpfully abbreviated, unjustifiably optimistic, alienating, and generally unhelpful, then it may be time to find new ways of talking about images that are not art.

What might happen when art and science are not privileged

This book is not my first attempt to find a way of thinking that could include all sorts of images at once. The other projects are relevant here, because they form the background and justification for this book. The first was *The Domain of Images,* which divides images first into three groups (writing, pictures, and notation), and then into a set of seven.[18] The triad writing, pictures, and notation was intended to capture the fact that mathematical images are used and talked about differently than written language or visual images. The division into seven was partly borrowed in part from Ignace Gelb, who was Derrida's source for "grammatology." The seven included allography (calligraphy, typefaces, and the visual elements of writing), subgraphemics (writinglike fragments of images), and emblemata (highly organized symbolic images). *The Domain of Images* is a long and complicated book, and it has the conceptual narrowness that any taxonomy imposes on itself. Its crucial limitation, as the art historian Robert Herbert pointed out, is that it has to renounce some of the history of the objects, and virtually all of their political and social contexts, in order to make sense of how they have

Critiques his own first attempt The Domain of Images

been read. Emblemata, for example, are interpreted in distinct and definable ways — they have an inner logic, a lexicon, and protocols of reading that make them recognizable and legible — but in order to analyze the differences between emblems and other, less organized images, it is necessary to suspend an interest in the history or social contexts of individual emblems. *The Domain of Images* subordinates the purposes images serve to the ways people interpret them, and in that respect it is, in the end, a formalism.

The book *How to Use Your Eyes* took an entirely different approach.[19] It has thirty-odd very short chapters — the length of the chapters in this book — describing such things as "How to Look at the Night Sky," "How to Look at a Twig," "How to Look at a Shoulder," "How to Look at an Engineering Drawing," and "How to Look at Sand." Each chapter gives as many names and terms as I could find about each subject: the half-dozen sources of light in the night sky aside from the moon and stars; the "leaf scars" that make it possible to identify trees in the wintertime; the names and motions of muscles in the shoulder. The book is full of pictures and unusual words. Half the chapters are objects made by people — the script Linear B, Japanese calligraphy, paintings, scarabs — and half are natural objects — moths' wings, sunset colors, twigs, grass, sand. *How to Use Your Eyes* is empirically minded, and was rightly said to depend on technical nomenclature: its methods do not work on objects that have few names or parts. As one reader said, it ends up making seeing into reading. I am not sure of the force of that claim, because it can be argued that the world only becomes visible through language, when an object has a potential name — but the book is certainly limited to visual objects that have already been extensively labeled.

How to look at BMW?

diagree about connection between visibility + language

The exhibition that is recorded here was my third attempt to speak about images in general, without the boundaries of fine art. It is more technical than *How to Use Your Eyes*, and more careful about the disciplines that produce knowledge than *The Domain of Images*. The exhibition was intended as an example of what the field of visual studies might accomplish if it were to relinquish its lingering interest in art. Visual studies continues to grow very rapidly but I think it effectively remains in an academic ghetto, confined by its concerns with mass media, fine art, and politics.[20] First-year classes taught as introductions to the visual world continue to take most of their examples from Western fine art and mass media, and to a lesser extent from design, craft, and non-Western practices. When objects outside of art are considered, they are treated in a general way, as examples of production or politics. Scientific and other non-art images are adduced to enrich the cultural contexts of fine art or to explain references in individual artworks. Science is seen indistinctly, from a distance.

(This is more true in North America and the U.K. than in German-speaking countries and in Scandinavia. There, visual studies is frequently more attentive to non-art images. Examples include Gottfried Boehm's "Iconic Criticism" initiative in Basel, Horst Bredekamp's work at the Humboldt-Universität Berlin, and individual projects in Karlsruhe, Copenhagen, Aachen, Stockholm, Magdeburg, Leipzig, and Lund. This book fits more with German-language scholarship than with English- or French-language work, which continues to stress political, gender, and wider social meanings. I explore this issue in the Afterword.)

The founding gambit of visual studies in English-speaking countries is that in a world of proliferating images, it no longer makes sense to have specialists on every conceivable kind of image, as it had once been useful for art history departments to have specialists on medieval, Renaissance, Baroque, and modern art. Visual studies posits that what matters is a more abstract, reflective concept of the production and dissemination of images, and a methodology capable of revealing the ways images are made to seem compelling and how they reform their viewers and shape their desires. That has been a fruitful direction for several decades, and it may continue to be: but it does not address what happens in the sciences, for the simple reason that it elides the specific content of non-art images even as it pays close attention to the specific content of art and mass media. The American World War I poster with the legend "I want you!" has been analyzed in several visual studies publications, but there is still nothing in visual studies that analyzes a gene map in such a way that a student could explain what its parts signify. The exhibition was intended to discover what it would sound like to pay attention to all images, art and non-art alike, with the level of detail used by their makers and their intended public. (Detailed engagement is, I think, indispensable: in this book, I made a few images myself, using scientific software and laboratory equipment — the opening images in Chapters 1 and 10, for example. Only by operating the instruments, and learning the software, is it possible to see the limits of a humanities-based visual studies.)

The exhibition was difficult for viewers, and likewise this book is not easy to read. Its chapters are like a collection of short stories: they have different characters and plots, but like stories by a single author, they share a number of themes, passing them back and forth, sometimes developing them, sometimes not. An editor who saw this book in manuscript said that it was too "particulate"; to her, the chapters seemed disconnected and too much concerned with the recitation of facts. This book is designed that way, instead of as a single continuous narrative, because I think that disjunctions are exactly what the field of visual studies needs in order to move forward. Texts on visual studies by W.J.T. Mitchell, Nicholas Mirzoeff, Mieke Bal, Don Ihde, and even Bruno Latour are limited by their strengths, as it were: they offer continuous theorizations in non-technical prose, but in doing so they exclude ideas that cannot be accommodated by humanities-style narration. What is at issue here, from the standpoint of visual studies, is the sense of appropriate theorization. The thirty practices in this book embody a number of themes, as I will propose below, but the individual visual practices are not subsumed by those themes. Discontinuous, "inappropriately" factual, surprisingly technical, "particulate," apparently under-theorized visual encounters are exactly what I think will produce a genuine advance in theorizing the visual, an advance that will propel visual studies out of the humanities and into the wider practices of the university.[21]

Five themes in this book

These are the problematics that emerged as the material for the exhibition was being gathered. They were not posed ahead of time, but worked out as the images were being discussed. In this book they are threaded through the chapters, appearing intermittently, providing what I'd like to call a discontinuous continuity. They are themes to bear in mind as you sample the book.

1. *How much of the world can be pictured?* When the proposals for exhibits started coming in, I was struck by the fact that some departments that I would have thought were very visually oriented had not responded. We had no proposals from the Departments of Process and Chemical Engineering, Electrical and Electronic Engineering, Politics, or Statistics. (There were a couple of near misses: a scholar in Statistics was thinking of investigating Florence Nightingale's statistical graphics of childbed mortality; and a lecturer in Electrical and Electronic Engineering was pondering an exhibit showing the potentially harmful radiation from a cell phone entering a listener's brain — he decided against it because it might be both misleading and disturbing.)

At the same time, we got a number of proposals from disciplines that are not especially known for their engagement with the visual. A member of the German Department proposed an exhibit of concrete poetry in German, and a member of the French Department proposed the *cadavre exquis,* the Surrealist game in which a figure is drawn on sections of folded paper, so no one can see the full monster until the paper is unfolded. Both would have been interesting exhibits, but we decided not to develop them because they did not seem representative of what scholars in those departments ordinary did. Concrete (shaped) poetry has been practiced in the German language since the middle ages, and there is wonderful material that would have been suited to an exhibition — garlands and elaborate knots made of micrographic script, entire pictures made of tiny letters — but concrete poetry was also made in Latin and in most European languages. The *cadavre exquis* is a visual game played from the 1920s onward, but it does not have a direct relation to scholarship in the French language. We had several other proposals along those lines. One display in the exhibition exemplifies that issue: Chapter 5, on Irish Ogam script, is a very specialized study of early Irish writing, as it is discussed in a particular medieval manuscript. The scribe assigns a color to each letter in the Ogam alphabet, making it into a system of hidden color symbolism. The scholar who prepared this material, Caitríona Ó Dochartaigh, wanted to make the point that it is very difficult to find visual material in her field. It took some sleuthing, and an especially arcane example, to locate visual interest in medieval Irish manuscripts.

Comparing the list of departments that routinely use images with those that normally do not, I noticed a disparity: most visual work in the university is done outside the humanities, but most of the claims to be doing visual work came from within the humanities. The large body of philosophic scholarship on relationships between the world and images can obscure the fact that visual images are peripheral to the concerns of people who work in the languages, and the same is true of linguistics itself. On the other hand, the routines of image making and image interpretation in fields such as chemical engineering can make it seem as though nothing of pressing interest needs to be said about the images themselves, because all that matters is what the pictures represent and the science they make possible. The most interesting question that can be asked of this, I think, is the extent to which the world, as it is seen from the perspective of any given discipline, seems to be amenable to visualization. How much of the world — that part of it studied by a discipline — can be pictured?

For some disciplines, the answer would be that very nearly everything of interest can be represented; for others, such as French or German, the answer might be very different. This question, and several I will be asking later in this Introduction, can be nicely exemplified by a multi-volume atlas of electrical engineering that I came across in a used book store. It's a thick, stubby book, intended as a handbook but too chunky to fit in a pocket. In exactly 2,100 thin pages and 3,773 tiny pictures it purports to illustrate every concept in electrical engineering.[22] A typical page on the different meanings of "zero" on analog meters shows how the book might be useful.

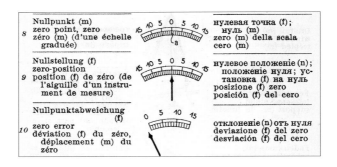

"Zero point," "zero position," and "zero error" are clearly distinguished in the pictures. But it is easy to overestimate what can be visualized. The page on Morse code is much less useful (read the illustration on the next page). It exemplifies Morse code with some samples, and then omits the Morse alphabet entirely for lack of space, even though it would have been reasonable to expect

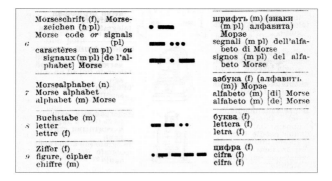

	Morseschrift (f), Morse-zeichen (n pl)	• ▬	шрифтъ (m) (знаки (m pl) алфавита)
6	Morse code *or* signals (pl)	▬ ▬ • • •	Морзе segnali (m pl) dell'alfa-beto di Morse
	caractères (m pl) *ou* signaux (m pl) [de l'al-phabet] Morse	▬ • ▬	signos (m pl) del alfa-beto Morse
7	Morsealphabet (n) Morse alphabet alphabet (m) Morse		азбука (f) (алфавитъ (m)) Морзе alfabeto (m) [di] Morse alfabeto (m) [de] Morse
8	Buchstabe (m) letter lettre (f)	▬ ▬ • •	буква (f) lettera (f) letra (f)
9	Ziffer (f) figure, cipher chiffre (m)	• ▬ ▬ ▬ ▬	цифра (f) cifra (f) cifra (f)

it to be illustrated. "Letter" and "figure, cipher" are then illustrated with their Morse equivalents, though I can't quite see why. Elsewhere in the book, the editor gives up entirely when it comes to illustrating concepts related to ponderability (the capacity of an object to be weighed). There are no illustrations at all for the page including "ponderability," "ponderable," and several grammatical variants.

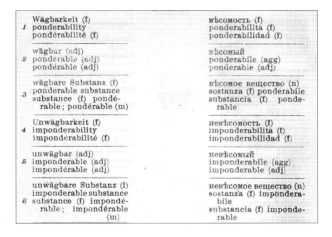

1	Wägbarkeit (f) ponderability pondérabilité (f)		вѣсомость (f) ponderabilità (f) ponderabilidad (f)
2	wägbar (adj) ponderable (adj) pondérable (adj)		вѣсомый ponderabile (agg) ponderable (adj)
3	wägbare Substanz (f) ponderable substance substance (f) pondé-rable ; pondérable (m)		вѣсомое вещество (n) sostanza (f) ponderabile substancia (f) ponde-rable
4	Unwägbarkeit (f) imponderability impondérabilité (f)		невѣсомость (f) imponderabilità (f) imponderabilidad (f)
5	unwägbar (adj) imponderable (adj) impondérable (adj)		невѣсомый imponderabile (agg) imponderable (adj)
6	unwägbare Substanz (f) imponderable substance substance (f) impondé-rable ; impondérable (m)		невѣсомое вещество (n) sostanza (f) impondera-bile substancia (f) imponde-rable

It is hard to judge how much of electrical engineering is amenable to being il-lustrated; my guess would be no more than a quarter of it.

This question, about how much of the interesting world can be pictured, is tricky. The chapters in this book imply answers ranging from nearly none of the world (as in Chapter 5 on Irish Ogam script, or Chapter 29 on words for "light" and "dark" in Russian and Arabic) to almost all of it. Chapters 15 and 26 are the ones that represent aspects of art history, my own field and the one that might seem most thoroughly visual among the humanities. Art history and its intermittent companion studio art do take visual objects as their principal subject of study, but that does not mean that they visualize those objects *economically.* It is easy to demonstrate that art history and studio art use visual objects that are more detailed than the disciplines can accommodate. Their excess visuality is a remainder, left untheorized or even unremarked.

Consider this nineteenth-century photoetching made after a print by Rembrandt.

Photoetchings have virtually the same detail as original prints; a teacher of mine once told me some Prints Rooms in museums used to bring out photoetchings to test novices. (If the young historian didn't know the difference between the photoetching and an original print, she would only be given photoetchings from then on.) For these purposes the photoetching has the full detail of an original impression. Plate 8 is a detail of it.

The next three plates show, in order: the best available reproduction in a book; the view a student in the back of a seminar room would have of the best slide of the print from the slide collection of the University of Chicago; and the best available image on the internet, which in many cases is all a student might be able to find.

The second-to-last picture was taken in a darkened seminar room, from a seat toward the back, so it is a reasonable representation of what a student would see.

The salient point here is that none of these images, except perhaps the last, would be an impediment to any of the existing art historical accounts of the print. What art history says about visual objects is routinely far less than what is contained in the objects. In a sense that's a truism, but it also points to a kind of excessive visuality, which itself has a value even if it is not articulated: in art history it means, roughly, that the objects are art.

Other disciplines are both strongly visual and also maintain a closer correspondence between the content of images and the content that is understood to be

significant. Here the preeminent field, as I write this in summer 2006, is probably the study of protein folding. It has only been possible to visualize molecular folding for ten or fifteen years, because of the computing power that it requires. Now some truly amazing films have been produced showing, frame by frame, the calculated positions of some very complex molecules. (At this point books are no longer the optimal medium, and I will be pointing to several URLs and laboratories rather than reproducing individual frames. It is best to read this with a computer at hand, and see the films for yourself.) The visualization of molecular movements began in the 1980s, when it became possible to calculate the static properties of molecules such as electron density surfaces. Some sophisticated versions of those early graphics, transformed into movies, are now routinely available.[23] The new movies reveal molecules as twitchy, shuddering things, not at all the way they had seemed in the many elegant and unmoving "ribbon diagrams" of older textbooks.[24] At the most sophisticated levels, distributed computing has made it possible to make animations of the folding of large molecules like t-RNA. Such molecules fold in thousands of similar ways, and by sharing the calculations across a number of computers, researchers have found the commonest path from unfolded to folded molecule.[25]

Protein folding animations preserve a closer correspondence between forms in the images and forms that are analyzed, simply because each "ball" or "stick" or "ribbon" (each component of a molecule in the animations) is calculated. In the art historical example, the sitter's hair and wrinkles, the texture of his clothes, and the play of light and shadow, are taken to be outside the purview of the discipline.

Massive, computed visualization of proteins is different from what is taking place in other disciplines that are equally entranced with the visual. Astrophysics is one such discipline, and another is the electron microscopic imaging of individual atoms. Both are concerned with the limits of what can be resolved using their instrumentation. Chapter 12 compares images of the Galactic center over the last thirty years as astronomers have looked more and more closely at the tiny area just around the very center of the Galaxy, where a number of stars orbit a black hole. Chapter 6 is about one of the current limits of resolution in astronomy, an ingenious technique that allows astronomers to exceed the theoretical limits of resolution of their telescopes and visualize the dynamics of binary stars. The imaging of individual atoms using various kinds of electron microscope is another example of imaging technologies that are concerned with the limits of instrumentation, but there is an interesting difference. Still images of atoms in crystal lattices can be fairly sharply defined, almost as if the atoms are little billiard balls and the pictured are just a little out of focus. But the laws of quantum mechanics make it impossible to sharpen the blur, whereas in astronomy it is always possible to imagine larger telescopes.

Movies of individual atoms can be wonderful to watch. The pixellated blurs that show the positions of the atoms — or, in other cases, the smoothed bumps that stand for atoms — move in and out of visibility, like soft little stars. In some movies atoms race around after one another, twirling under the influence of mutual attraction and speeding apart when repulsive forces become stronger.[26]

One of the masters of this medium is Jan-Olov Bovin of Lund University; his films show individual gold atoms hovering over the surface of a gold crystal, shifting in and out of visibility, as if they were thinking about landing on the crystal.[27] Again I hesitate to reproduce individual frames. In the hands of the best technician, like Bovin, the movies are strange and compelling.[28]

I have briefly opened four questions within this first theme, just to show how rich it is. Within the question of how much of the world is understood to be visual, there are also the questions of the non-visual nature of the humanities; the unthematized, excess visuality of disciplines like art history; the profligate visuality of fields such as molecular biology; and the interest in the limits of visuality in fields like atomic physics. When I said that genuine theoretical progress can only be made by paying close-grained attention to the languages of different disciplines, this is what I meant: whole books could be written about each of those four sub-themes.

2. *Abuses of the visual.* Sometimes images accompany research papers, conferences, and textbooks, even though they are not used to support the science. In some fields images are customary; they are made habitually, and their absence

would seem odd. As the exhibition developed, it became clear that a fairly high percentage of the production of images across the university was of this kind: images were expected, but it wasn't always clear what function they fulfilled. I call these occurrences "abuses" just to give them a provocative label: I don't mean that images are used wrongly, just that they are unexpectedly *not* used, or used for unexpected purposes given their contexts. I will distinguish four kinds of abuses: visualization that is habitual, compulsive, forced, and useless.

Habitual visualization. A good example of the first is Chapter 24, which explores a blue and white image of the proteins in Cheddar cheese. The scientist who sent me this image, Paul McSweeney, at first thought I would use it as it was, without much explanation. If I had, it might have become one of the "beautiful" images that are thought to communicate some of their content simply by their aesthetic appeal. We wrote back and forth about his image, and it emerged that his laboratory does not always make such images, even though his research was on the subject of proteins in cheeses. Much less "beautiful" versions of the image are good enough for research purposes, and in fact they do not even need to be dyed blue. But every once in a while the lab needs a "beautiful" image to advertise itself. Gel electrophoretograms, as they are called, are a stock-in-trade of such laboratories; they are made for the posters scientists display at conferences, for teaching, for the covers of scientific journals, and for publicity inside and outside the university.[29] Labs that use gel electrophoresis are typically capable of producing these more "beautiful" versions of their ordinary images on demand.

In this book another instance of habitual visualization is in Chapter 8, which describes a software package called Nagios, used to keep an eye on computer systems like those found in large companies. Nagios normally runs in the background, but if there is a problem with one of the company's servers or with its internet connections, the full-screen view gives information about each component of the network. One of Nagios's selling points is its "3-D" view of a network, which displays servers and computers connected to one another by a web of lines, rendered in simple perspective. David O'Byrne, the computer scientist who introduced me to this software, said that he doesn't actually use the 3-D view. He prefers the tabular view or the 2-D map because when there is trouble, they give more information than the 3-D view. Nagios sells in part because of its capacity to produce useless, "pretty" pictures. In this case as in the Cheddar cheese images, visualization is habitual or customary, but not necessarily pertinent.

Compulsive visualization. My little encyclopedia of electrical technology is full of pictures that seem to have been made under a nearly incomprehensible compulsion to picture everything. One page offers vignettes of different kinds of "shops": machine shops, erecting shops, pattern shops, repair shops (see the illustration on the next page).

I can't recognize anything in them except a few workbenches. I wonder for whom these could possibly be useful: if I had an intimate knowledge of German

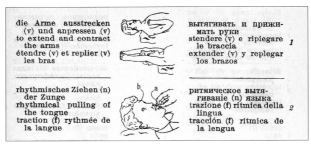

machine shops in the 1920s, then I might find it helpful to compare the pictures of different shops, but somehow I doubt it. My favorite section in the encyclopedia is the one on first aid, which includes pictures of a man who has fainted, together with instructions on how to extend and fold his arms in order to revive him, and even how to pull his tongue.

I have no idea why it was considered helpful to pull an unconscious person's tongue, but the encyclopedia shows how to do it, and even labels the tongue and the man. The compulsive production of pictures is — one might argue, following for example Jean Baudrillard — a feature of late capitalism in general, but its disciplinary forms have not yet been studied. It occurs in this book in several forms; the most intriguing is Chapter 19, where a mathematician shows how to solve a problem once posed by Lewis Carroll using a series of graphs. His effort is part of an on-again, off-again tradition of visualizing mathematics: Should mathematical truths always be susceptible to being visualized? Or is the truth non-visual, and images its ornament? It's a foundational disagreement, played out most lucidly in mathematics. The mathematician who devised the visual solution to Lewis Carroll's problem didn't need to do so, but he was interested in the possibility. There is a compulsiveness about some scientists' use of the visual, and a compulsiveness about other scientists' refusal of the visual. The project in Chapter 19 is too extensive to illustrate in this book — it ran to over fifty diagrams — but it effectively demonstrates that the problem can be solved using entirely graphical means.

By *forced visualization* I mean the habit of making pictures of objects that are non-visual because they are multidimensional or not susceptible to illumination. Quantum mechanics is the twentieth century's pre-eminent example. The objects it describes are famously outside of ordinary human experience and possibly of all spatial intuition. Paul Dirac, one of the most acute theorists of quantum mechanics, is often quoted for his mistrust of images and his injunction to physicists to just "follow the mathematics" no matter how strange it might seem.[30] On the other hand there are specialists in quantum physics who do the opposite: they go on making pictures of quantum phenomena, despite the fact that they have to bend pictorial conventions to uses they had never had.[31] Bernd Thaller is the best example I know; he has written books and computer programs, and produced CDs of his visualizations. He makes pictures and movies of quantum effects, showing how particles exhibit wavelike behavior when they encounter objects.

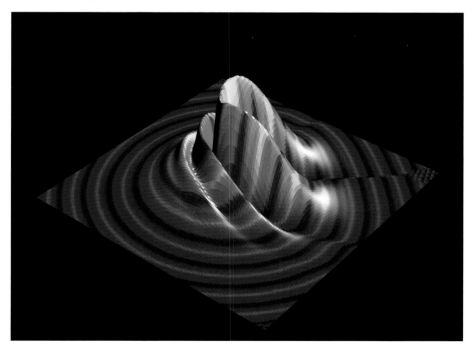

His images are colorful because he symbolizes the phase of the wave equation by colors assigned to the complex plane: a positive real component is red, decreasing in chroma in proportion to its distance form the origin, a positive imaginary component is yellow-green, and so forth. I mention this for readers who may be interested; the salient point is that the colors are only one of several properties of the particle's wave equation. Other properties have to go unvisualized because it simply isn't possible to put them all into a picture or a movie. Most fundamentally, the wavelike objects Thaller visualizes aren't waves, but probabilities, in accord with quantum mechanics, and that basic difference is one of the reasons some quantum physicists eschew pictorial representation altogether. Everything about such pictures, it could be said, is a misleading analogy based on familiar, human-scale phenomena. Thaller is an optimist about representation, a complement to Dirac's pessimism. He is very inventive at bending the usual functions of pictures to make them express the maximum amount about the unimaginable objects described by the mathematics. He "forces" the conventions of pictures to express properties of objects that can never be seen — much less seen as waves or as color.

Useless visualization. In 1999 I visited a laboratory at the University of North Carolina at Chapel Hill, where a scientist named Richard Superfine was investigating carbon nanotubes.[32] He had several atomic force microscopes set up in the lab, trained on microscopic samples of the nanotubes. Sitting at a monitor, I saw a flat surface in perspective, with a wobbly form lying on it like a bent pipe. At my right, in front of the monitor, was a pen, attached by a series of bars and joints to the desktop. As I moved the pen, a cursor on the screen moved. The idea was that I could actually push the nanotube around on the substrate, and that when I made contact, the pen would push back, representing the force required to move the nanotube. The universal joint attached to the pen would provide force-feedback, giving me a kinetic sense of the object's tensile properties and the forces binding it to the substrate. Superfine's laboratory had several such microscopes, which they used to investigate the ways nanotubes bend, roll, and stack — the ultimate aim being to build structures with them, possibly even nanodevices such as nanobots. I asked for some scientific papers that set out discoveries made with the atomic force microscopes, and Superfine said there weren't any — that his results came from other experiments. That surprised me, and I asked what the force-feedback devices taught them. He said they kept a list of "aha!" moments, in which people in his lab had found unexpected properties of the nanotubes by pushing them around, but that none of those "aha!" moments had made it into a scientific publication. The microscopes were wonderful, he said, for getting a feel for the objects, and they were also popular with school tours. They helped publicize and promote the lab's activities, and they gave an intuitive grasp of the objects, but they did not produce science. The science came from more controlled experiments, in which properties such as tensile strength and compressibility could be quantitatively measured.

A "useless" image, in science, can be defined as an image that cannot be used to calculate, because it has nothing quantitative in it. Superfine's force-feedback setups are useless in that sense. There are also images that have quantitative information, but the experiments choose not to extract it. Instead the people who make the images are interested in them as visual examples of what their equations would look like. There are some spectacular examples in recent science. A Hungarian team produced a short film of a scanning tunneling microscope tip hovering over a carbon nanotube, just the kind of arrangement that Superfine's laboratory had.[33] In scanning tunneling microscopes, a sharp tip (the inverted cone at the top) senses the object, in this case a carbon nanotube (the hollow tube at the bottom). In practice, such a microscope would be used to produce a picture of the object — the nanotube — as if it were seen from above, and that is the way I observed nanotubes in Superfine's lab. In the Hungarian scientists' movie, what's under study is the microscope itself. The carbon nanotube is modeled as

a cylinder 0.5 nanometers in diameter, and time is measured in femtoseconds. As the viewer watches, a slippery-looking sheet comes down over the tip and envelops the nanotube, as if it were a dessert being covered with liquid white chocolate.

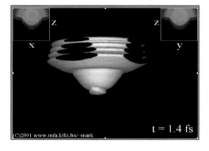

The white goo is the constant-probability surface of a Gaussian wave packet. It is an amazing visualization, and the mathematics behind it are pertinent for the design of such microscopes — but the film itself does not provide the analysis, only the visualization.

An even more impressive example is Farid Abraham's simulation of the motion of 1 billion atoms in a block of copper (see the illustration on the next page).[34] It is a film made to show the effects of putting copper under stress but not breaking it: the atoms shear against one another, producing dislocations throughout the block. The film includes several fly-throughs of the block,

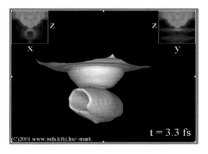

and viewers can watch as the dislocations spread like tendrils throughout the mass of copper.

(Atoms are only drawn if they are dislocated by the pressure: the film actually represents a solid block of a billion atoms, but the only ones shown are along shear lines.) Interesting as the film is, it only gives a qualitative idea of the tangle of dislocations; the science is elsewhere. It is useless, strictly speaking, because it serves more to capture viewers' imaginations than to disclose new properties of copper.

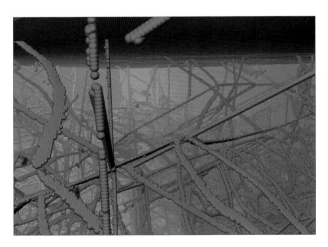

It might be said that the "abused" images in these four categories aren't "useless" at all, because they serve political ends. They help laboratories and scientists advertise themselves, and they spark conversations about the work that may lead in new directions. That is true; the images are only "useless" in the sense that they themselves are not the proof or evidence of whatever scientific claims the laboratory is making. They are, instead, ornaments on the more fundamental work of experiment or mathematics. I called this theme "abuses of the visual" rather than, say, "images that are only political" because the word "politics" flattens the images' different relations to scientific truth and utility. The politics of publicity, grants, careers, and publications certainly contributes to the production of "useless" and other "abused" images, but politics isn't the whole story. In the humanities, and especially in visual studies, the politics of an image is nominally its most fruitful and constitutive property. Politics is taken to go, as Nietzsche said, "all the way down," and analyses can begin and end with the politics of image-making and image interpretation. In the sciences, politics plays a crucial role but it is not what the enterprise is all about. The idea of thinking about "abuses of the visual" is to shift the conversation a little so that these images cannot be so quickly explained as politically expedient.

A salient fact here is that the sciences, unlike the humanities, produce enormous numbers of images they do not directly use. To some degree these "useless" images are evidence that people associate truth with images, so that an image is a proof of veracity even when it is does not, strictly speaking, prove anything. It makes sense, I suppose, that such images are common in the sciences than in the humanities, where veracity and truth are so much to the point. It might be fruitful to study these "abused" images from this perspective, as remnants of the idea that images are truth. (One could ask, for example, what about each image seems to capture something true, even though that truth cannot be quantified or linked to the mathematics or the experimental data.)

Images that are made and discarded, made but not used, made but not valued, are ubiquitous, and one of the cardinal dangers of any study that emphasizes images is not noticing when the objects of study aren't valued by the people who make them. The field of visual studies, and in particular those scholars, centers, and departments interested in non-art images, are liable to make too much of what they study, and not to notice when the objects are eclipsed or forgotten. "Abused" images are also a reminder that it is easy to overvalue the objects of one's attention. Many of the pictures in this book are simply not important to the fields that produce them.

3. *What counts as a picture?* I have mentioned the fact that some images in this book look like naturalistic pictures, but aren't. The images in Chapter 12, for example, are "velocity graphs." In a normal, naturalistic picture of something — say, a galaxy — an object higher in the picture would be "higher" in space (perhaps in declination, to use the astronomical term), and an object to the right in the picture would be "to the right" in space (in right ascension, say). In Chapter 12, the two axes of the pictures do not represent position, but speed. The images look like ordinary photographs of astronomical objects, but they aren't.

Should such images be counted as pictures, or would it be better to call them graphs or — following the three-part division in *Domain of Images* — notations? Sonograms are another example. The song of the Canyon Wren reproduced in Chapter 8 looks like a picture of the bird's song, but of course it isn't: it's a graph of the pitch of the song as it changes through time. Readers accustomed to music notation will be able to "read" the graph in a general way, and see how the song drops down in pitch. It's the kind of song that people call "sad" or "plaintive." The sonograms of human speech reproduced in the same Chapter are harder to "read" but they are constructed the same way. It would probably be stretching the concept to call these pictures, but it would also be appropriate because they are constructed to look a bit like pictures. It often helps scientists to have images that behave *a little* like ordinary naturalistic photographs.

That extraordinary fact opens a new way of talking about such images. They are *picturelike,* and the right language for interpreting them should probably not be too far removed from the language that is used to interpret naturalistic images. If they were simply or purely graphs or notations they might well be arranged differently: without glowing colors, for example, and without higher tones being higher on the image. Those are pictorial conventions, borrowed from ordinary picturemaking. All sorts of different conventions would be available to image-makers who did not want to keep the residue, the hint, of ordinary pictures.

It is possible to distinguish several different kinds of images that are not quite pictures:

Picturelike graphs. The examples I have given so far substitute things like pitch, time, and velocity for the usual dimension of space. (A photograph is a space-space representation, to put it abstractly. A sonogram is a pitch-time representation, and the images of the galactic center are velocity-velocity representations.) Even the spectrum that opens Chapter 1 is picture-like. Its vertical axis indexes wavelength, and its horizontal axis is meaningless. (Aside from the film strips at the right and left, which are used for measuring.)

Multidimensional images. Chapter 16 reports on an aerial survey of Cork done with a specialized camera, like one later flown on a mission to Mars. The camera gathered a mass of data, which was used to produce aerial photographs that look just like old-fashioned aerial photographs taken with simple cameras. But those familiar-looking images were *extracted* from the mass of data the camera gathered, which could be used to generate all sorts of other images. The team that flew the camera over Cork used the fuller data set to study the height of buildings and to make a simulation of the flooding of the city. The data could also be used to identify specific crops, or distinguish fallow fields from planted ones, or to survey tree cover — there is a large potential range of agricultural, geological, engineering, and city planning applications. The aerial photographs are thin slices of a larger data set.

The same could be said of the 3-D laser surveys of inscribed stones described in Chapter 22, or even the encyclopedic map of the geology of southwest Ireland shown in Chapter 14. Both result in pictures that are only samples of the available data. This kind of thing rarely happens in the arts and humanities. The *Mona Lisa* is not an extract from some larger bank of images, except in the abstract sense that it has a history and a context, like any image. Artworks tend to display or contain the sum total of their information, but scientific images are sometimes just tiny portions of a larger invisible or unvisualized whole.

Frankenstein pictures. Then there are images cobbled together from many different sources, not all of them visual. A curious example is a film of the binary star system named Wolf-Rayet 104 (the name identifies one of the two stars in the system). The system, WR104, has been widely reproduced as a short film loop because of the very unusual fact that it looks like a pinwheel.

In the film, the spiral spins. The effect is caused by hot gases being thrown off of one of the stars in the pair. (Neither star is directly visible in the image.) The popularity of the film must be due in part to the surprise of discovering that somewhere in the constellation of Sagittarius there is a little pinwheel spinning.

Yet the film is really very distant from a movie of a pinwheel-shaped object. First, its "hot" red color is false.[35] Actually, it was imaged in the infrared, so this particular shape would be invisible to the naked eye. Second, this was never seen from a single telescope. It is an image constructed from three telescopes situated a small distance from one another in a field. Third (and most counter-intuitive), none of the three telescopes produced an image on its own. They each saw just one point of light at a time, and their signals were combined using interferometry. The combination of the signals of two of the three is shown below; that is a stage in the construction of the pinwheel image.

Fourth, the signals processed to make the image underwent a change known as *heterodyne reduction:* they were each combined with laser light, producing a single wave of a much longer frequency, which was then carried as a *radio* signal in wires. Fifth, the reduction was necessary because the signals have to reach the computer that analyzes them at the exact same time, and the telescope at one end of the field is actually a tiny bit father from the star than one at the other end of the field. To compensate, the signal from the closer telescope is sent through a longer wire. It seems implausible, but in this way the three telescopes are effectively exactly the same distance from their object (the folded wires can be seen in the schematic).

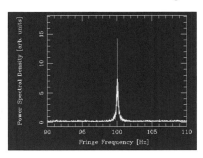

The pinwheel image was therefore built out of the signals from three telescopes, by heterodyne reduction, signal delay, interferometry, and false color: hardly an ordinary way to make an image.

Interferometry of this kind, which generates 2-D images, is both counter-intuitive and complicated, and although I have tried I cannot understand it in full. The deceptively

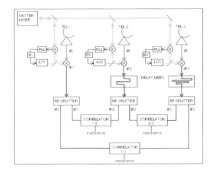

familiar-looking pinwheel is a Frankenstein creation, made of disparate parts. There is nothing quite so elaborate in this book, although the images of inscribed stones in Chapter 22 are roughly equivalent. They begin as "point clouds" (sets of 3-D data points recording the shapes of the stones) and end, after many layers of processing, as apparently naturalistic images that are actually composites of surface corrections, 3-D manipulations, lighting routines, false color, and texture mapping. They seem to raise the same issues of realism as the computer-generated monsters in Hollywood movies — except that the images of inscribed stones, and the film of WR104, began with observations of real objects.

Picturelike graphs, multidimensional images, and Frankenstein pictures are examples of things that aren't really pictures or films in the conventional senses of those words. The aerial photograph in Chapter 16 is only a conventional picture if its matrix is ignored: really, it's a sliver of something larger, like the portion of a multidimensional geometrical object that can be represented on a piece of paper. The Wolf-Rayet star, velocity graphs (Chapter 12) and speech sonograms (Chapter 8) are picture *mimics:* they work, in part, because the mimic pictures.

4. *The thicket of representation.* This is a phrase coined by the biologist and philosopher William Wimsatt to describe the problem of making pictures of genes.[36] There are a half-dozen different conventions for making pictures of complex organic molecules, and no one of them is adequate by itself. Each gives a particular kind of information, and works at a certain level of detail. Ribbon diagrams of molecules, for example, do not quite reach to the level of atoms, but ball-and-stick models do (compare the top and bottom of the illustration on the next page).[37]

These two images cannot be combined into one image because they use different imaging conventions; it would be like trying to paste a picture of your house onto a map of your town. In scientific software these two conventional representations can be "toggled," but they can't be fused into one kind of picture.

This is another theme that is largely unknown in the humanities. A close parallel might be the existence of a painting and a drawing for the painting: the two can't be combined, but they have to be considered together in order to get the fullest idea of the artist's conception. The flaw in that parallel is that in most cases, the painting was intended to be the self-sufficient and authoritative version of the object; in science, all the kinds of representation in the thicket need to be considered together. The authoritative version of the object is not any one visual representation, but a conceptualization that involves a number of different kinds of images.

In this book, a good example is the visualization of bacteriophages in Chapter 27. The Chapter lists eight different ways of making pictures of bacteriophages. They vary tremendously, from ordinary close-up photography of Petri dishes to complicated graphics of individual atoms. More could be added to the list. I have

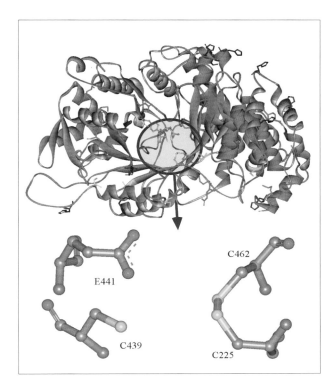

mentioned Hybrid Medical Animation's dramatic movies (see the illustration on p. 16). Another is Steven McQuinn's 3-D renderings of the head capsids of a bacteriophage; he uses translucent surfaces to make the subtlest structures visible (see illustration on the next page). (In Steven's case, the idea isn't to do science, but to tweak the scientists' assumptions about what microscopie objects might "look like." He intentionally uses translucent surfaces and ray tracing to make the viruses look like plastic bottles.[38])

There are also a few scanning electron microscope images of bacteriophages, and I could add life-cycle diagrams (a common feature of biology textbooks for at least fifty years), and even spectrographs.[39] On a rough count that is thirteen ways of looking at bacteriophages, although the number is arbitrary because most kinds subdivide into different types. A typical scientist might use a half-dozen in different combinations, toggling back and forth to compare them, and printing several side by side in scientific papers. The thicket cannot be cleared: it can only be negotiated.

In this book, you can explore the thicket of representation in most of the chapters. The exceptions are subjects where just one kind of image is optimal (Chapters 7, 17) or where images really aren't the point (Chapter 24). The arts, again, are the odd man out: Chapters 15 and 26 on fine art do not have competing images. Even ar-

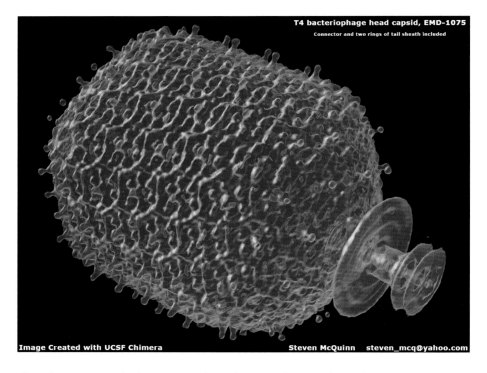

T4 bacteriophage head capsid, EMD-1075
Connector and two rings of tail sheath included

Image Created with UCSF Chimera   Steven McQuinn   steven_mcq@yahoo.com

chaeology, among the humanities, has a ferociously complicated repertoire of imaging types, many of which are used together to describe archaeological sites (Chapter 13). The thicket is the norm, and the isolated image of fine art is the rarity.

5. *Image quantification.* If there is a general, underlying expectation of images in the sciences it is that they contain what I call *propositional content.* It is expected that data can be extracted from them, that they contain measurable forms. A bar graph can be read immediately for its information, and so can the kind of supply-demand graph used in economics (Chapter 4). Other images have to be measured before information can be extracted from them; an example is astronomical images, which are read pixel by pixel to extract quantitative information. The analogue in the humanities would be images that are also writing, so they can be read as well as seen, as in Chapters 5 and 29. It is normal in the sciences to analyze an image in order to extract information, and anything that is left over is considered heuristic, decorative, "aesthetic," or "beautiful." A striking image can be a good thing, if it helps the image attract attention, but what matters is the content, stuff that can be used to calculate. It is more or less the opposite in the humanities, where propositional content in an artwork — themes, ideas — would normally be seen as an interesting part of the work, but by no means its central quality. The lack of interest in propositional content explains why art historians (I was one of them) were impatient with David Hockney's and Charles Falco's

explanations of the perspective and geometry of paintings: it wasn't that Hockney was wrong, exactly, but that his observations were beside the point.[40] John Heartfield's political collages, studied in Chapter 26, are not valued because of what they say about Hitler — many other people during the Weimar Republic accused the Nazis of similar things — but because of their visual form. It is the extra, what is taken as the visual contribution, that matters in fine art.

It is interesting to study how scientists, lawyers, doctors, and engineers search for propositional content. Often the tool is image-analysis software, which can outline objects of specified shapes, sizes, or colors. The geologist Pat Meere uses software to find the outlines of grains embedded in rocks (Chapter 23). The biologist Emer Rogan uses software to find the outlines of the fins of whales and dolphins (Chapter 25), and Marc Shorten uses similar software to trace the outlines of the wings of ducks and other birds (Chapter 18). All three outlining routines are different. Image-analysis software is ubiquitous in this book. It can also color-code objects of interest, such as frequencies in sonograms (Chapter 10) or crops in a field (Chapter 16). It can count objects, and even produce equations for their shapes (Chapter 23). In the humanities, there really isn't such a thing: it is only the sciences and allied fields where the quantification of images is important. Image-analysis software is a big and largely unstudied field; the major software packages, such as Exbem, NIH Image, and ImageJ, are virtually unknown outside the sciences. (Photoshop, the image manipulation software of choice in the arts, has only very limited image analysis capabilities.) Scientific image analysis software packages are the equivalent of the exotic kinds of diggers that are used in large-scale strip mining: they are the most efficient way to strip away the "aesthetic" and get at the informational.

It is fascinating that some image-making practices outside the arts continue to resist quantification. An example is mammography, which despite all efforts to automate it continues to require expertise and, as a necessary correlate, to be considered less than wholly reliable. In the mid-twentieth century the same was true of the diagnosis of chest X-Rays for signs of tuberculosis. Having been tutored in how to read X-Rays, I can say that it is definitely an art (that is, a skill that cannot be wholly taught) to spot the small white smudges that are the first signs of tubercular infection. They are hard to see, and hard to distinguish from vessels seen end-on. Experts in chest X-Rays and mammograms tend to be people who have practiced for years.

In this book the preeminent example is the physician Nollaig Parfrey's discussion of kidney diseases (Chapter 21). Parfrey is an expert on membranous glomerulopathy, a condition that is not easy to diagnose. It requires a series of images made using different image technologies — it's an example of the thicket of representation. Each image needs to be analyzed for qualitative, rather than quantitative, signs. The relative abundance of some forms, or the relative thickness of capillary walls, are clues. Only a few of the signs Parfrey looks for are unambiguous forms that are either present or absent. Medical semiotics, I think, is the best example of a discipline that seeks to extract propositional content from images, but cannot always do so. Its images are qualitative, but they are studied for quantitative information.

Image quantification, and the search for propositional content, is terra incognita for the humanities. A visual studies scholar, looking at these examples, might be interested in the human interactions that result from Parfrey's analyses (some of which require biopsies), or in the reasons some scientists *want* to measure with such sweeping techniques and such obsessive precision. Visual studies might be good on the politics, the sociology, the psychology of image analysis: but it remains the case that image analysis itself is an enormous advance in the interpretation of images, made within the last twenty years, and it has been virtually ignored by scholars interested in the uses and meanings of the visual.

Those five themes — deciding how much of the world can be pictured, cataloging abuses of the visual, wondering what counts as a picture, exploring the thicket of representation, and learning about image quantification — structure this book. They do not make these chapters into a unity, because that would play false with the diversity of imaging practices, but they should be kept in mind as you read. Other themes — I'll mention a few more below — could easily be found; that's why it's a wonderful subject.

The idea of a university-wide course

In 2006, I supervised a course called "Visual Practices Across the University," with guest lecturers from the exhibition. It was the first of its kind in Ireland and the UK, because it was open to all students, in all faculties of the university, and at all levels. It was intended to test the possibility that images might be a way of introducing students and faculty to the full range of disciplines in the university.

One issue we mulled over was how many kinds of image production, or image interpretation, there are. If there are as many kinds as there are departments, then studying visual practices across the university would just be studying as many examples as feasible in a given time. There would be no possibility of ever getting a sense of the whole, and possibly no way to achieve a satisfactory articulation of themes like the five I have just enumerated. But as we worked through the material, the ways of making images and the ways of interpreting them started to fall into groups.

The first, and perhaps most apparent, distinction is between disciplines whose image-making practices are technical and those that appear not to be. Nominally, all departments in a university practice and represent a *discipline,* with all that word implies. Given that disciplinarity has its own ideology, and that it often privileges technical knowledge that cannot easily be gained by other disciplines, it is to be expected that most of the examples in this book, and in the class, required preparatory study. But not all of them. Bernadette Sweeney's practice of documenting performance art and theater is non-technical in the sense that the problems it raises can be set out fairly quickly. In Chapter 2, Sweeney outlines the problematics of documenting transitory art forms like theater, and she brief-ly mentions the literature in which critics have said that "time arts" (such as film and performance) require a new sense of documentation, and a new kind of art criticism. That literature is large, and so is the literature on the technical, philo-sophic, and political aspects of documentation. But Sweeney's practice can be shown relatively easily, and it does not present itself as technical. The questions it raises (Is this an adequate document of the performance? Is it biased in some way?) can be pondered by any viewer.

Likewise the contributions by the Departments of Occupational Therapy (Chapter 9) and Applied Social Studies (Chapter 20) have no technical language. The former is an exercise to help children become socialized by making art; and the latter is a workshop on social identity, in which participants make and wear masks of themselves. In both cases a technical exposition would be inappropriate because the purpose of the work is to create new social bonds among people who are not members of any particular discipline. The same observation could be made of Chapter 7, in which a lawyer reports on the use of a "virtual-reality" system to help witnesses recall what happened during an event in which a num-ber of people were killed. Anything technical in the system would have put off the witnesses, and it would not have been helpful to the tribunal, which was try-ing to find the maximum amount of information about the event.

Two chapters display the non-technical side of science. In Chapter 3, the geologist Bettie Higgs shows what can be deduced by just looking at weathered sandstone rocks found on a seashore. Higgs brought rocks into the class and had people lift them — some were fairly heavy — and consider their properties and their age without prior information and without magnifying lenses. She considers that kind of preliminary inspection an integral part of geology. She calls it "artistic" as opposed to "scientific," but I would prefer to say simply "non-technical" and "technical," because the "scientific" examination requires technical knowledge. (She also brought a polarizing microscope into class, so students could see birefringence phenomena; but analyzing those phenomena requires technical knowledge.) Chapter 11 is probably the oddest thing in this book: it is a discussion of the colors of porcelain teeth by two experts in restor-ative dentistry. It was a popular display in the exhibition, because visitors were invited to learn the system and then look in a mirror and classify their own teeth. (Those of us who gave tours to the public suggested that people learn the color nomenclature of their own teeth, and then surprise their dentists by asking for specific colors.) There is real color science in Chapter 11, because it turns out that teeth come in all the hues of the rainbow, but the colors are reduced to subtle shades of off-white, so they are extremely difficult to spot. But even the color science is not technical, and the end purpose is an "aesthetic" match, meaning in this case a feeling, on the part of the patient, that the porcelain tooth matches perfectly.

So a first look at visual practices suggests they might divide between those that depend on technical information known only in certain disciplines and those that employ non-technical or non-disciplinary words to describe images. I have not pursued that distinction, for two reasons. Most apparently, it depends on dubious senses of what is technical: people in the humanities say the sciences are technical, but the same can be said about some of the humanities because it isn't clear what counts as technical language. More importantly, the distinction has to make use of an ideology of disciplines according to which the sciences and medicine are safely walled enclaves of the obscure.

More promising groupings began to appear as soon as the planning for the exhibition was underway. Optical microscopy, for example, formed a group across several disciplines, including polarized-light microscopy (in geology), fluorescence (in biology and medicine), phase contrast, and interference contrast (in biology). They comprise a kind of group, in the sense that a person who knows one can pick up the others.

My electrical engineering encyclopedia has many examples of images, and kinds of images, that fall into such groups. About ten pages, for example, are devoted to the ways wire is wrapped in coils to make motors.

		послѣдовательно-параллельная (смѣ-шанная) обмотка (f)
5	Serien-Parallelwicklung (f) series-parallel winding enroulement (m) *ou* bobinage (m) série-parallèle *ou* mixte	avvolgimento (m) in serie parallelo arrollamiento (m) en serie y paralelo
6	Trommel-Parallelwick-lung (f) parallel drum winding enroulement (m) *ou* bo-binage (m) parallèle en tambour	барабанная парал-лельная обмотка (f) avvolgimento (m) a tam-buro in parallelo arrollamiento (m) en paralelo de tambor
7	Trommel-Serienwick-lung (f) series drum winding enroulement (m) *ou* bo-binage (m) série en tambour	барабанная послѣдо-вательная обмотка (f) avvolgimento (m) a tam-buro in serie arrollamiento (m) de tambor en serie
8	Ring-Parallelwicklung (f) parallel ring winding enroulement (m) *ou* bo-binage (m) paralléle en anneau	кольцевая параллель-ная обмотка (f) avvolgimento (m) ad anello in parallelo arrollamiento (m) de anillo en paralelo
9	Ring-Serienwicklung (f) series ring winding enroulement (m) *ou* bo-binage (m) série en anneau	кольцевая послѣдо-вательная обмотка (f) avvolgimento (m) ad anello in serie arrollamiento (m) de anillo en serie

I have no doubt that if I applied myself, I would soon be able to tell the difference between "parallel-drum winding" and "series drum winding," and if I worked at it, I would eventually be able to name all fifty or so windings.

The motor windings portion of the electrical encyclopedia is like a little trea-tise, separate from the other 2,050 pages of the book. I want to draw some paral-lels between circumscribed subjects like these and the visual practices in this book, but first let me add a few examples. First is a lovely little book I found called *Argumes / Citrus Fruit,* published by an international committee for the standardization of citrus (see the samples on the next page).[41]

The pamphlet offers just a few criteria to help wholesale grocers and farmers distinguish between Second Class, First Class, and "Extra" Class lemons and or-anges. The pamphlet does not go into the hundreds of varieties of citrus, and the technical nomenclature is minimal. The conceptual difficulty here is distinguishing what is meant by "light" damage as opposed to "heavy," or what is "superficial" as opposed to "deep." The number of terms is minimal, but they are slippery.

Andrew Aandahl's *Soils of the Great Plains* (1982) is an atlas of about a hundred soil types in central North America (illustrations on the second and third page following).[42]

Each page has a sunny photo of a landscape, and a photograph of a cut-away section of the soil, and a technical analysis of the soil layers. The right-hand por-tion of each cut-away section has been smoothed with the back of the shovel, so it reflects light differently. The purpose of the atlas is to enable farmers to iden-tify their soil types, ideally without having to cut cross-sections. If I were to

Texte interprétatif de la norme	Interpretation of the standard

ATTEINTES CICATRISÉES DUES A UN TRAUMATISME (suite)

Meurtrissures (Dommages causés par choc ou pression sans rupture de l'épiderme)(Variété Navel)

Bruises (Damage caused by shock or pressure without the skin being broken) (Navel variety)

Catégorie «Extra»

"Extra" Class

Catégorie I
- légère
- superficielle
- non étendue

Class I
- slight
- superficial
- not extensive

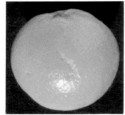

Limite admise — Limit allowed

Texte interprétatif de la norme	Interpretation of the standard

ATTEINTES CICATRISÉES DUES A UN TRAUMATISME

Lésions superficielles de grêle (le terme «superficielles» s'applique à l'aspect de la zone déprimée. D'une manière générale, on peut admettre que les lésions sont considérées comme superficielles lorsque l'épiderme n'est pas profondément déchiré et/ou que les diverses taches n'affectent qu'une faible surface) (Variété Shamouti)

Injuries superficial, caused by hail ("Superficial" applies to the appearance of the area affected. Generally speaking, injuries may be regarded as superficial when the skin is not torn and/or the individual blemished are only small) (Shamouti variety)

Catégorie «Extra»

"Extra" Class

Catégorie I
- légères

Class I
- slight

Limite admise — Limit allowed

Texte interprétatif de la norme	Interpretation of the standard

HEALED INJURIES DUE TO ACCIDENTS (cont'd)

Catégorie II
- sans lésion sensible de la pulpe
- peu étendue

Class II
- without appreciable damage to the pulp
- not extensive

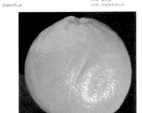

Limite admise — Limit allowed

Admis dans les tolérances de la catégorie II

Allowed within the tolerances for class II

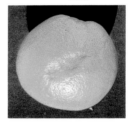

Texte interprétatif de la norme	Interpretation of the standard

HEALED INJURIES DUE TO ACCIDENTS

Catégorie II
- assez légères

Class II
- fairly slight

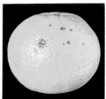

Limite admise — Limit allowed

Admis dans les tolérances de la catégorie II

Allowed within the tolerances for Class II

study this book while I drove around the Midwest in the United States, I would eventually be able to make a guess about soil types without needing to do any digging. There is a technical vocabulary to be learned here, and a list of a hundred soil types to be memorized, but if this were the subject of a class, it could be done in, say, a few weeks. *A Classification of North American Biotic Communities* (1998) is different because the criteria for identifying each biotic community is much less well defined (see illustration on page 49).[43]

Irrigated corn on level Hall soils. In the Great Plains most of the corn grown for grain is irrigated. Many Hall soils in the uplands have buried soil, as seen in the profile below. The soil to a depth of 80 cm is in a more recent deposit of loess. Hall soils often receive extra water from adjacent slopes. This soil profile picture also illustrates the color differences between dry and moist soils.

HALL SOILS

Ap   0–20 cm (0–8 in.). Grayish brown silt loam, very dark grayish brown, moist; slightly acid.

A12   20–45 cm (8–18 in.). Dark grayish brown silt loam, very dark brown, moist; weak fine granules; neutral.

B2t   45–80 cm (18–31 in.). Brown silty clay loam, dark brown, moist; moderate medium blocks; clay skins on peds; firm; neutral.

A1b   80–110 cm (31–43 in.). Dark grayish brown silt loam, very dark brown moist; weak medium subangular blocks; friable; neutral.

C1ca 110–130 cm (43–51 in.). Grayish brown silt loam; massive; friable; few gray limy masses, calcareous.

C1   130–150 cm (51–59 in.). Light brownish gray silt loam; massive; calcareous.

Geography: Central Nebraska and north-central Kansas.   183

Soil Family Classification

Sorghum and winter wheat on level Harney soils. Large grain elevator in the background. These are common in the Great Plains and usually one is in sight wherever there is considerable acreage of cropland. A few tracts of these soils have native vegetation consisting of little bluestem, sideoats grama, buffalograss, and blue grama.

HARNEY SOILS

A1 0–25 cm (0–10 in.). Dark grayish brown silt loam; moderate medium granules; firm; neutral.

B21t 25–45 cm (10–18 in.). Grayish brown silty clay; strong medium and coarse blocks; firm; mildly alkaline.

B22t 45–60 cm (18–24 in.). Pale brown silty clay; strong, medium and coarse blocks; very firm, moderately alkaline.

B31ca 60–112 cm (24–44 in.). Light yellowish brown silty clay loam; moderate coarse blocks; firm; few small masses of soft lime and limy coatings on peds, calcareous.

IIB32b 112–155 cm (44–61 in.). Brown silty clay loam; weak coarse subangular blocks; firm; few small limy masses; calcareous. (This horizon is part of a buried soil formed in an older loess with a reddish tint. Buried soils are common below Harney soils, but they are not always present.)

Geography: West-central Kansas.

187

Soil Family Classification

Fine, montmorillonitic, mesic Typic Argiustolls

Each caption names only a few plants that are typical of the community: for "Central American Thornscrub," for example, we are told only that "the shrubbery is punctuated by a columnar cactus, a cholla, and an arboreal prickly-pear, as well as numerous small trees." Elsewhere in the book the listings are expanded, but there are no definitive or comprehensive enumerations of the plants that

Plate 108. Arctic-Boreal Marshland (241.). A tiny sedge-populated *ciénega* of Rocky Mountain Subalpine Marshland located at 2740 m (9000 ft) atop the Pinaleño Mountains, Graham County, Arizona. Photo by D. E. Brown.

Plate 109. Cold Temperate Marshland (242.). A Great Basin Marshland located at Ruby Lake, Elko County, Nevada. The principal marsh emergents are roundstem bulrush (*Scirpus acutus*) and cattail (*Typha latifolia*). Photo by D. E. Brown.

Plate 113. Warm Temperate Strand (253.) represented by California Maritime Strand at Scammon's Lagoon, Baja California Norte, Mexico. This sparsely vegetated community on a mud substrate, although a true wetland, is reminiscent of, and analogous to, the desertland formation of upland vegetation. A stand of cordgrass (*Spartina* sp.) forms a marshland in the background. Photo by D. E. Brown.

Plate 112. Cold Temperate Strand (252.). A U.S. Park Service photo of Oregonian Maritime Strand taken in February 1961 by Louis G. Kirk at Rialto Beach, Olympic National Park, Washington.

are typical of each biotic community. Such a listing would be open-ended, because biotic communities overlap, and it would be too long to put in a book. So to identify the biotic communities, a reader needs to note where the community is (the book is accompanied by a map), and then get a "feel" for it. My response to this book varies depending on whether or not I am already familiar with the kind of landscape in the photo. I know "Arctic Boreal Marshland," and I recognize the feel or the look of the place. If I have ever walked through "Central American Thornscrub," I am unaware of it, and it seems only faintly familiar, as any arid hillscape might be. This is a more difficult subject than the Midwest soils, which are in turn more difficult than the citrus guide, and all three are harder than the listings of motor windings.

I am suggesting that these are subjects that are similar in complexity to the image-making practices in this book. I think it helps to imagine these four books, and the individual Chapters of this book, as if they were languages, either in Wittgenstein's sense of toy languages (imaginary languages with just a few words) or in the ordinary sense. I do not mean anything especially profound by this. In particular I am not implying anything about underlying structures, as in Chomsky or Jerry Fodor. Nor do I mean to suggest that these languages have some relation to differing epistemologies of the world, as in Benjamin Whorf's work, or even to different kinds of intelligence, as Howard Gardner has argued. And I am not saying these are languages in a philosophic sense, in Nelson Goodman's or Quine's sense.

I mean something more prosaic and practical: like languages, these subjects can be learned to a reasonable degree of proficiency in a reasonable amount of time. The time required is keyed to the structure of university disciplines, so that it takes a year or two, sometimes three, to become adequately proficient at most of the visual practices in this book. That time scale allows students to shift subjects, and add areas of expertise, within the frame provided by the university. (Of the four books I have mentioned, only the last two are difficult: I imagine learning motor windings and grades of citrus would take only a semester.)

The university scale of the time it takes to learn the visual practices in this book is the first analogy with languages. The other is that the visual practices in this book occur in groups, as I suggested in the case of light microscopy. Like languages, they come in families. For a person who understands phase contrast microscopy, interference contrast microscopy will already be partly intelligible. A person who knows interference contrast microscopy will know some of the fundamentals of polarized light microscopy. The same affinities occur in natural languages. A person who knows Danish will be able to understand Norwegian and parts of Swedish, but such a person will not be able to follow spoken Finnish or Estonian, because they belong to different language families. In the university, the language families of visual practices cluster in related departments.

Provisionally, then, the language families of the *construction* of images include the following: (a) optical microscopy, comprising about five languages; (b) image analysis software (NIH Image, ImageJ, Exbem, Photoshop); (c) digital video editing; (d) mapmaking and surveying in archaeology and civil engineering; (e) electron microscopy, including transmission, scanning, and atomic force microscopy, all of them represented in this book. There are perhaps a dozen others: my claim would be that the number of "language families" is not the same as the number of disciplines or departments in a university, but is a significantly smaller number. That is crucial to this project, because it means that visual practices can be studied across the entire university. If there is a preeminent language family of image construction, analogous to Indo-European among natural languages in Europe, it is not fine art but scientific and technical image manipulation: another reason to say the humanities are in the minority when it comes to images.

These "languages" can also be enumerated from the side of image *interpretation*, in which case I might list: (a) X-Rays and mammograms, (b) histology, (c) cognitive psychology and the neurobiology of vision, and (d) the history of art, which has about a dozen named languages in this sense including psychoanalytic art criticism, deconstruction, semiotics, and feminisms. Again there would

language families for image-making

be about a dozen more, all told. There is an often implicit claim among visual studies scholars that image interpretation is theorized mainly in the humanities, but if there is a preeminent language family here it would be medical semiotics. The kinds of interpretations of histological material given in Chapter 21 represent an enormous set of practices with a long history, stretching back to ancient divination using animal organs. By contrast the humanities own only a small number of ways of interpreting images.

(This enumeration of language families, both in image construction and interpretation, may be compared to the much larger sample in the book *Bild und Erkenntnis,* edited by Andreas Beyer and Markus Lohoff.[44] Their book surveys many more technologies, and groups them according to an eclectic glossary of "visualization techniques" such as "Modell," "Notationssystem," "Objektklassendiagramm," "Phasendiagramm," "Piktogramm," "Prototyp," and "Radardiagramm." I find their book interesting as a resource, but I am more optimistic about organizing the material into a smaller number of conceptual units.)

In outline this is how I would defend the idea that visual practices can be studied all together, and that they can be learned to a workable degree of detail in, say, a year-long course. Such a course would have several advantages over existing introductions to the visual world. It would be *specific,* and need not rely on general observations about image production and dissemination. Existing introductory classes on visual studies or visual appreciation stay mainly within the fine arts, because the sciences, medicine, law, engineering, and other fields are out of reach unless students are introduced to their actual, day-to-day discourses, in detail and without undue generalization. (Students would have to learn some mathematics and physics, for example, in order to understand the images of carbon nanotubes I mentioned. That is impractical but not at all impossible, providing the instructors are available.) I think the existing first-year classes on visuality and visual culture are more rewarding for students who go on to study in the humanities than they are for students who study the sciences, because the level of detail of the art examples is so much higher than the detail accorded to the few non-art examples. A student majoring in chemistry, for example, will probably not think back on her first-year visual studies class when she is busy with molecular imaging: but she would if she had the experience of encountering molecular imaging in her first year in college, in the context of imaging done in other fields.

A second advantage of a year-long course on visual practices is that it does some justice to the commonplace that ours is a visual culture, where learning is increasingly done through images. There is a large literature arguing that visuality is the preeminent medium of our experience of the world, but universities continue to pursue text-based and mathematics-based education. This class would put visuality on the table in the first year of college as a subject and a central vehicle for understanding the world.

A final reason I am interested in using materials like the ones in this book for a university-wide course is that it could provide the beginnings — the first impetus — for university-wide conversations. The visual can be an informal *lingua franca* for the university, allowing people who would not normally stray outside of, say, inorganic chemistry, to consider starting conversations with people in, say, Asian studies.

Despite the interest in interdisciplinarity, universities are not usually unified in more than name. Students begin to specialize in their first few years, and by the time they are ready to begin graduate study they are already focused on just a portion of one subject in one Department. In the Irish and UK systems, it is normal for students reading medicine to have no arts courses at all, and vice versa. Many initiatives are being developed to prevent that, but it is inevitable given the degree requirements of different fields. The Law Faculty might as well be in a different city from the Agriculture Faculty or the Engineering Faculty. In the US it is said that "distribution requirements" and "core requirements" compel students to take classes outside their major fields, and that is true, but the number of courses is small, and the selection is narrow. In a typical case a student in Arts may have to take one science course and one social science course. In that mix Dentistry, Medicine, Food Processing, Pharmacology, Business, and any number of other subjects are omitted. The university is still unified in name only.

I do not think that this book could be a panacea for the fragmented life of the contemporary university. Even if it were two hundred chapters long, accommodating every department and named subspecialty in a large university, it would still only be a provisional cross-section, a sampler like my 2,100-page encyclopedia of electrical engineering. But I am convinced that this is a way to discover whether the university is a single thing, or just a collection of buildings in which people speak mutually unintelligible languages.

The literature on the unity of the university is itself based in the humanities, and biased toward them. (It is also a very non-visual literature: not a single book I have seen is illustrated.) Like Cardinal Henry Newman's *Idea of a University* (1852), Jaroslav Pelikan's book of the same name (1992) has next to nothing to say about the sciences. Henry Hutchins, one of the principal theorists of the University of Chicago, argued in *The University of Utopia* (1964) that nothing should be taught in the university except philosophy. Other books, from Clark Kerr's *Uses of the University* (1963) and Kenneth Minogue's *Concept of a University* (1973) to Bill Readings's *University in Ruins* (1996) and Jacques Derrida's essays collected in *Eyes of the University* (2004), are similar in their emphasis on philosophic "rights" and philosophic analysis. Ultimately they all owe that emphasis to Kant, whose theorization stressed the importance of the Faculty of Philosophy over the "vocational" Faculties of Law, Medicine, and Theology. The fairly enormous literature on the idea of the university is strongly biased to the humanities, and exclusively non-visual. I'd like to think this book is a small step toward a different theorization.

I would also like to distinguish this book from certain parts of the current interest in interdisciplinarity. Traditionally, the idea of interdisciplinarity is traced to Wilhelm von Humboldt, whose ideal of the university has gone through many transformations. An excellent book by R. D. Anderson, *European Universities from the Enlightenment to 1914* (2004), distinguishes Humboldt's ideas from the notion of them held in the nineteenth century, and the different notions attributed to him in the twentieth century.[45] In the nineteenth century it was still remembered that the purpose of studying all subjects together was to reveal *Wissenschaft,* properly signifying the unity of all knowledge. That Romantic ideal, which I suspect few people believe today, was the original rationale for what is now known as interdisciplinarity. By the twentieth century, the Humboldtian ideal was held to be the research university, which was conflated with the Romantic idea of interdisciplinary work. Many university systems in the United States are said to be derived from the German university system, meaning the Berlin University and specifically Humboldt, even though we have long forgotten the Romantic ideal of unified knowledge and we have misinterpreted Humboldt's interest in research (which was always tied to teaching).

Today, with the Humboldtian heritage forgotten, there seem to be several other reasons for promoting interdisciplinarity. In Europe, interdisciplinary initiatives are sometimes said to be done in emulation of the US. Interdisciplinarity is also said to enable universities to be more economically efficient. A university financial officer in Ireland once told me that interdisciplinarity in the European Union is modeled on the success of "big science" such as the Manhattan Project and CERN. Interdisciplinarity has been a byword in the humanities since the spread of poststructuralism, although it is not clear to me whether the humanities' sense of interdisciplinarity has influenced the current worldwide interest in interdisciplinarity, or has just happened to coincide with it. It is interesting that those three explanations for interdisciplinarity — emulation of the US, efficiency modeled on big science, and the influence of poststructuralism — are different and even mutually contradictory.

My own interest in exploring interdisciplinarity came partly from talk about interdisciplinarity in the humanities. Visual studies claims itself to be interdisciplinary in a new and interesting fashion, creating a new form of knowledge that is more than the simple juxtaposition of its component disciplines. It is still hard to tell whether or not that is happening, but it is likely that visual studies is an amalgam of disciplines and that each one is retaining much of its original nature.[46] There is at any rate no evidence of a radical, self-transforming interdisciplinarity in the Chapters of this book. The Chapter with the largest number of specialties involved is Chapter 22, on the laser scanning of inscribed stones. It involves a physicist, a computer scientist, and people with expertise in epigraphy, church history, Latin, Irish, literary theory, and education. But it is collaborative rather than transformative: each person contributes expertise to a project whose ultimate purpose is the preservation of cultural heritage. I suspect that the epistemologically challenging interdisciplinarity (or "transdisciplinarity" or "subdisciplinarity") sought in visual studies is not something that most interdisciplinary ventures outside the humanities would seek even if they knew about it.

I do not know what sense of interdisciplinarity is enacted by this book. Given that theorizations of the university are still done from within the humanities, that the original impetus for interdisciplinarity has long been forgotten, that the reasons now given for it are so diverse and mutually contradictory, and that the utopian transformative interdisciplinarity envisaged by visual studies may not exist — given all that, it is probably best to avoid the subject for the time being. For the duration of this book, at least, let us just listen to how images are talked about in their own disciplines, and contemplate the possibility that they might coalesce just enough to make a constellation, as Mallarmé says in *Un Coup de dés* — something new, that may have a meaning we can only just glimpse. I think what is lost by spending some time with these occasionally arcane, particulate practices is more than repaid by the sheer expanse of the view outside the confines of fine art and visual studies. And in any case what reasons do we have, aside the many habits of art, to keep our distance from so much of the visual world?

Notes

1   The main set of papers in the conference, with contributions by W.J.T. Mitchell, Barbara Stafford, Jonathan Crary, and others, will appear as *Visual Literacy*, edited by James Elkins (New York: Routledge, 2007); a second set of papers on the subject of the histories of individual nations and their attitudes to visuality and literacy, will be forthcoming as *Visual Cultures*.

2   eb.mit.edu/i-m/intro.htm. My review of the 2001 conference is "Who Owns Images: Science or Art?" *Circa* 97 (2001): 36-37, online at recirca.com/backissues/c97/elkins.shtml.

3   web.mit.edu/felicef/.

4   In this context I am only giving the outline of the argument: an example is discussed in detail in my *Domain of Images* (Ithaca NY: Cornell University Press, 1999).

5   Hester, quoted in Frankel, "Sightings," *American Scientist* (September-October 2004): 463. The most through work on the subject is beeing done by Elizabeth Kessler, whose work I found, unfortunately, just after this MS went to press. Her interviews with astronomers are very illuminating for the questions I raise here.

6   Try www.thomaskinkade.com; there are many other sites and stores.

7   Smock, "Picture This!" in *California Monthly* (March/April 2005), pp. 16-27.

8   www.dna11.com, accessed March 2006. I thank Curtis Bohlen for drawing my attention to this.

9   Thomas Rossing and Christopher Chiaverina, *Light Science: Physics and the Visual Arts* (New York: Springer, 1999). See the review by Henry Stroke in *Physics Today* (May 2001): 60; Stroke notes the asymmetry of the book, which concentrates on the influence of science on art, and notes that artists sometimes influence science. His example is Leopold Godowsky, Jr., and Leopold Mannes, who invented the Kodachrome process; but Stroke observes they both also had physics degrees.

10 His website glosses his book by claiming that "despite what appear to be irreconcilable differences, there is one fundamental feature that solidly connects... evolutionary art and visionary physics. [They] are both investigations into the nature of reality. Roy Lichtenstein, the pop artist of the 1960s, declared, 'Organized perception is what art is all about.' Sir Isaac Newton might have said as much for physics." It would be extremely difficult to find another artist who says that, and just as hard to define what it might mean. What art is made from "disorganized perception"? And what is "evolutionary art" anyway? Shlain, at www.artandphysics.com.

11 Gilardoni, *X-Rays in Art: Physics, Technique, Applications* (Mandello Lario, Italy: Gilardoni, 1977); Latham, *Art After Physics,* exhibition catalog, Museum of Modern Art, Oxford, 1991 (Oxford: The Museum, 1991); Shlain, *Art and Physics: Parallel Visions in Space, Time, and Light* (New York: Morrow, 1991).

12 The most promising project along these lines is John Onians's research at the World Art Studies Centre at the University of East Anglia, which is a patient and systematic search for things that particular branches of science — especially neurology — can say about art.

13 Notably David Stork and Charles Falco. My responses are a review of David Hockney, *Secret Knowledge* (New York: Viking, 2001), on the College Art Association review site at www.caareviews.org/hockney.html, and a review of the NYU conference in *Circa* 99 (spring 2002): 38-39; online at recirca.com/backissues/c99/elkins.shtml. The paper I delivered at the conference is at webexhibits.org/hockneyoptics/post/elkins.html. I have also rehearsed these argument in "Aesthetics and the Two Cultures: Why Art and Science Should be Allowed to Go Their Separate Ways," in *Rediscovering Aesthetics,* edited by Tony O'Connor, Frances Halsall, and Julia Jansen (New York: Columbia University Press, forthcoming).

14 Winner, "Art History Can Trade Insights With the Sciences," *Chronicle Review* (*Chronicle of Higher Education*) 50 no. 43 (July 2, 2004): B10, accessed online at chronicle.com, November 2004.

15 webexhibits.org/hockneyoptics

16 I am not criticizing all technologically-oriented art; my main target is the perception of the mainstream art world. For a full argument see my "Preface" to Eduardo Kac, *Telepresence and Bio Art: Networking Humans, Rabbits, and Robots* (Ann Arbor MI: University of Michigan Press, 2005).

17   This point is elaborated in my review of Martin Kemp, *The Science of Art* (Yale, 1990), *Zeitschrift für Kunstgeschichte* 54 no. 4 (1991): 597-601, and later in *The Domain of Images*.

18   *The Domain of Images* (Ithaca NY: Cornell University Press, 1999).

19   *How to Use Your Eyes* (New York: Routledge, 2000).

20   The argument I am alluding to here is given in my *Visual Studies: A Skeptical Introduction* (New York: Routledge, 2003).

21   One more project needs to be added to this sequence. From 1998 to 2002 I worked a book called *Six Stories from the End of Representation,* which will appear roughly at the same time as this book. It considers six fields, two in the arts and four in the sciences, and studies them in six separate chapters. (*Six Stories from the End of Representation: Painting, Photography, Astrophysics, Microscopy, Particle Physics, Quantum Physics* [Stanford: Stanford University Press, forthcoming]). I make no connections at all between the six fields, and I do not present any over-arching theme. The idea is to let each discipline speak in its own words, in full technical detail, and not to popularize anything. *Six Stories From the End of Representation* is a kind of reductio ad absurdum of this book: it goes at great length into just six fields, instead of sampling thirty fields, and it declines all opportunities to make connections, whereas here I entertain whatever possibilities present themselves. *Six Stories* is intended to display the weaknesses of popularizing and abbreviating, and to pay whatever cost may be entailed in terms of readability.

22   *Die Elektrotchnik,* vol. 2 of *Schlomann-Oldenburg Illustrierte Technische Wörterbücher,* edited by Alfred Schlomann (Munich and Berlin: R. Oldenburg, n.d.).

23   See the demonstration of different parameters by James Holton, at ucxray.berkeley.edu/~jamesh/.

24   Two examples: Kay Hamacher's animation of protein-ligand docking at www.kay-hamacher.de (which is very suggestive, and would have delighted the Surrealists), and the high-speed snakelike folding of a 64-residue protein done by the Process Systems Engineering team at the University of California at Davis,
www.chms.ucdavis.edu/research/web/pse/research_areas/protein_folding_dynamics/protein_dynamics.php.

25   Eric Sorin et al., "Does Native State Topology Determine the RNA Folding Mechanism"? *Journal of Molecular Biology* 337 (2004), with online supplement, including a very complex animation, at folding.stanford.edu/tRNA/.

26   See the IBM research page "Imaging Atoms at Sub-Angstrom Resolution with a Corrected Electron Microscope," at domino.research.ibm.com/Comm/bios.nsf/pages/sub-a.html, accessed February 2006. "[W]hen two of them approach, they feel an attractive force. As they approach closer, this attractive force turns into a repulsive force. This can be seen in real time: summarized by the frames labeled by time. In this case, two atoms approach, circling one another (indicated by the arrows). Then one of the atoms moves rapidly away to a spot about 0.5 nanometers distance away. Finally the other atom follows."

27   Jan-Olov "Bob" Bovin: bob.materialkemi.lth.se/. I discuss these images at length in my *Six Stories from the End of Representation,* forthcoming.

28   See especially the films of oxidation on the surface of a Platinum-group metal by Bastiaan Lambertus Martinus Hendriksen at www.physics.leidenuniv.nl/sections/cm/ip, which reports on Hendricksen, "Model Catalysts in Action: High-Pressure Scanning Tunneling Microscopy," PhD thesis, University of Leiden, 2003.

29   Electrophoretograms are discussed in my *Domain of Images,* chapter 3, in reference to a study by Karin Knorr–Cetina and Klaus Amann, "Image Dissection in Natural Scientific Inquiry," *Science, Technology, and Human Values* 15 no. 3 (1990): 259–83.

30   Dirac: "one can tinker with one's physical or philosophical ideas to adapt them to fit the mathematics," he said, "but the mathematics cannot be tinkered with. It is subject to completely rigid rules and is harshly restricted by strict logic." Dirac, "The Mathematical Foundations of Quantum Theory," in *Mathematical Foundations of Quantum Theory,* edited by A. R. Marlow (New York: Academic Press, 1978), 2.

31   "On Some Useless Images [in Physics]," *Visual Resources* 17 (2001): 147-63; I will discuss the subject at length in *Six Stories From the End of Representation,* forthcoming (as in n. 21).

32   See for example www.rpi.edu/~huangh/workshoppdf/03LectureByDonaldBrenner.pdf.

[33] See www.nanotechnology.hu, and Márk Géza, I. Biro, P. László, and Philippe Lambin, "Calculating of Axial Charge Spreading in Carbon Nanotubes and Nanotube Y-Junctions During STM Measurement," *Physical Review* B 70 (2004); and see the preprint at www.mfa.kfki.hu/int/nano/reprint/prb_70_115423_3d.pdf.

[34] Farid Abraham of IBM Almaden Research, in collaboration with LLNL personnel Mark Duchaineau and Tomas Diaz De La Rubia; www.llnl.gov/largevis/atoms/ductile-failure/.

[35] The following is from isi.ssl.berkeley.edu/system_overview.htm#optics.

[36] This is discussed in my *Domain of Images,* together with further references.

[37] For the ribbon diagram see www.stjude.org/structural-biology/0,2540,432_2059_11435,00.html; for the ball-and-stick model, see www.ticam.utexas.edu/CCV/gallery/molecular-images/.

[38] McQuinn informs me that his ironies have been somewhat lost on scientists. Part of the problem is that the optimism about visualization is ubiquitous, and working scientists adopt rendering routines developed for Hollywood and for design. See for example the field ion microscope image of atoms in a tungsten needle, rendered as if the atoms were raspberries covered in syrup: www.aip.org/png/2006/264.htm.

[39] For spectroscopy of bacteriophages see nmrresource.ucsd.edu/posters/thiriot02.html.

[40] Hockney, *Secret Knowledge.* In addition to the essays I mention above (loc. cit.), there is a longer discussion in my *Visual Studies.*

[41] *Agrumes / Citrus Fruit,* in the series *Normalisation internationale des fruits et légumes / International Standardization of Fruit and Vegetables* (Paris: Organisation de Coopération et de Développement Économiques, 1980).

[42] Andrew Aandahl, *Soils of the Great Plains* (Lincoln NE: University of Nebraska Press, 1982).

[43] David Brown et al., A Classification of North American Biotic Communities (Salt Lake City: University of Utah Press, 1998).

[44] *Bild und Erkenntnis: Formen und Funktionen des Bildes in Wissenschaft und Technik,* edited by Beyer and Lohoff (Munich: Deutscher Kunstverlag, 2006); the glossary is on pp. 467-538.

[45] R. D. Anderson, *European Universities from the Enlightenment to 1914* (Oxford: Oxford University Press, 2004).

[46] This is discussed at length in my *Visual Studies.*

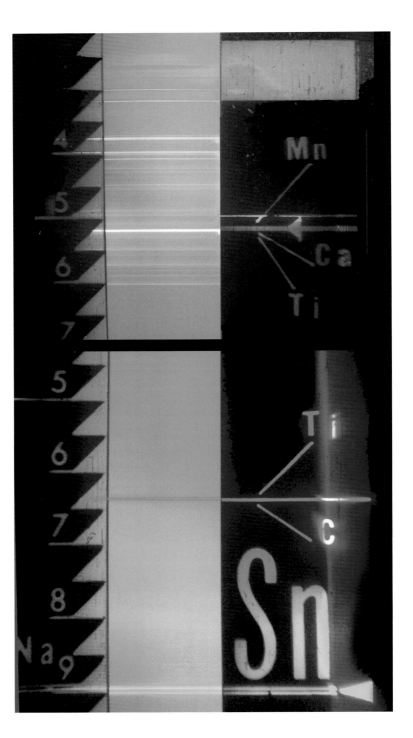

1

Spectroscopy
Pierre Laszlo and James Elkins

The large photograph is a spectrum. It records the wavelengths of light, from the deep violet near the end of the visible spectrum (at the top) down into the warmer colors that lead to infrared (at the bottom). The machine that made this is a Vreeland spectroscope, a fairly ugly machine that works very simply.

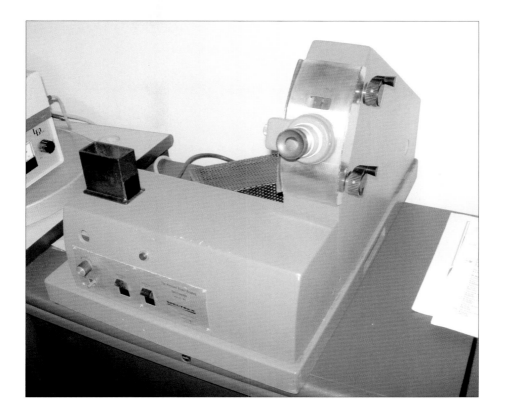

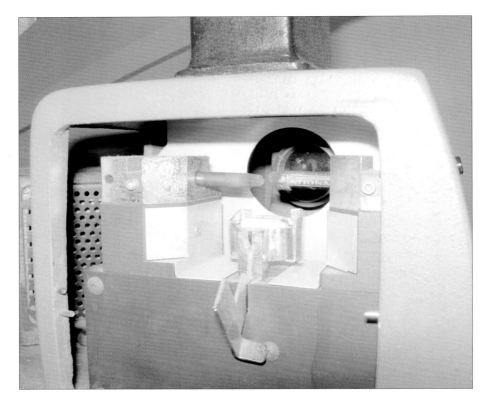

The sample, usually powdered rock, is put on a small ceramic plate; the plate is just visible beneath the dark opening. Above the plate are two carbon rods, which are arranged so they do not quite touch. When the machine is turned on, an arc of electricity sparks between the plates, creating a rasping noise and a blinding light (far brighter than sunlight). The arc melts and vaporizes the rock sample; the spectrum is produced when light is reflected off a diffraction grating inside the machine.

When a viewer looks in the eyepiece, he or she sees the spectrum in brilliant colors. The Vreeland spectroscope has two film reels that can run on either side of the spectrum. They can be rolled along using the two black handles visible in the first photograph. The left-hand film reel, in this case, has the wavelengths of light on it, for reference. The right-hand reel has the spectral lines that are characteristic of different elements. Here the large "Sn" indicates this is the portion of the film that shows the typical lines of Tin. The green line and the blue line match lines in the spectrum, and in fact the powder on the crucible in this case was pure tin from a chemical supplier.

From color to monochrome

This is simple spectroscopy, done with a rough-and-ready machine that was designed to be used in the field, by geologists. Machines like this are rare in laboratories now; they have been replaced by massive, and massively expensive, machines that produce very accurate quantitative results.

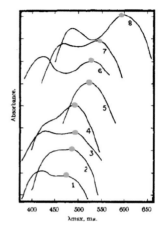

It may come as a surprise that spectroscopy, in science, does not often involve any color reproductions. This is a series of ultraviolet spectra, numbered 1-8, illustrating an experiment carried out in an organic chemistry laboratory during the 1950s — that is, almost exactly a full century after Bunsen and Kirchhoff invented spectroscopy.

The curves show how the molecules absorb light of different wavelengths. Note that there are no spectral colors here, and really no colors at all; the original publication had no red dots, and this was its only illustration.

What are we looking at?

The picture on the top depicts a stack of spectrograms — spectra for short. Each spectrum is that of a different molecule, numbered 1-8. The underlying physical phenomenon is absorption of light, in the UV-visible part of the range of electromagnetic radiation, that is, from 400 to 800 mμ (a micron, μ, is a millionth of a meter, or a thousandth of a millimeter).

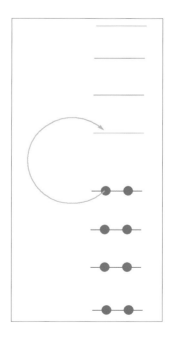

Why do certain molecules absorb light in that range? Because absorption of a photon lifts an electron — hence the name "electronic spectroscopy" — from a doubly occupied energy level (blue) into a vacant energy level (red).

As the light excitation sweeps through the accessible range, in this case from 400 to 650 mμ, it probes various electronic energy levels within a given molecule. The manifold of such light absorptions, across the whole range monitored, is termed the "spectrum."

The iconic language of chemical formulas

The simplest formulas, termed berzelian formulas, provide information only about composition. For instance, the methane molecule (natural gas) is CH_4, benzene C_6H_6 and hydrocyanic acid is HCN. In these, C stands for carbon, H for hydrogen and N for nitrogen.

A major step forward was taken during the 1860s when structural formulas were devised. They show in how atoms are connected. The very same examples are shown below:

Chemists soon realized that rather strict rules governed these formulas. Notice, for instance, how each carbon atom bears a total of four lines (bonds) to neighboring atoms? Accordingly, a shorthand was quickly established: one would display only the framework of interconnected carbon atoms without showing explicitly the attached hydrogen atoms. Thus, the benzene molecule is written, in this simplified manner as shown at the lower left.

In a benzene ring, all twelve atoms are in one and the same plane. To distort a benzene ring from such coplanarity demands considerable energy.

During World War I, Gilbert N. Lewis (1875-1946), a professor of chemistry at the University of California, proposed to integrate the then newly discovered electron into the structural formulas. Each line (bond) is equivalent to a pair of electrons. For instance, there are three such pairs between the C and N atoms in HCN. Moreover, there exist also pairs of electrons which remain uninvolved in bonding atoms. In the same HCN molecule, one such pair sits on nitrogen:

It remained for Linus Pauling (1901-1994) to perfect this iconic language by making the representation somewhat more involved. Consider again the HCN example. The three pairs of electrons in between C and N are drawn towards the atom on the right (N) since its nucleus has an additional proton. Protons have a positive electric charge, electrons are negativelycharged. Thus, protons attract electrons. To account for such a polarization, Pauling wrote the HCN structural formula as a *hybrid* of two limiting forms:

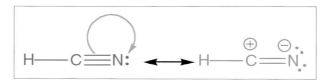

The red curved arrow shows transfer of an electron pair, from in-between C and N, to the N atom only. In the purple limiting form on the right, N has gained negative charge, from now bearing two instead of just one lone pair of electrons. Carbon, having lost negative charge, has become positively-charged. The HCN molecule is best conceived of as a hybrid (indicated by the black double arrow) of the two formulas in blue and purple.

What "physical organic chemistry" consists of

In chemical history, physical organic chemistry, which appeared during the 1920s and 1930s, was another hybrid. Organic chemistry studies molecules derived from hydrocarbons such as methane or benzene. Physical chemistry, a close relative of physics, studies the equilibria between molecules and the rate of the chemical reactions which interconvert them. Physical organic chemistry is thus physical chemistry applied to organic structures.

A defining trait of physical organic chemistry is the synthesis of novel molecular architectures in order to test theories of chemical structure. For instance, about the time Cram and Bauer published their paper, Philip E. Eaton, from the University of Chicago synthesized cubane.

In that structure with berzelian formula C_8H_8, the angles at the eight carbon atoms are constrained as 90° instead of the "natural" angle of 109.5° found in methane. What would be consequences of such a huge internal strain in the cubane molecule, Eaton wondered. We now know that one such consequence is the feasibility of manufacturing much more powerful explosives than previously known.

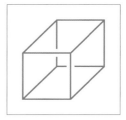

What are paracyclophanes, and why make them?

Donald Cram, in an early line of research, chose to synthesize paracyclophanes for similar reasons as Eaton's in making cubane. Paracyclophanes are molecules in which two benzene rings are bridged at positions diametrically-opposed, by a number of hydrogen-bearing carbon atoms. This is, for example, the formula of [2.2]paracyclophane (shown below, in blue).

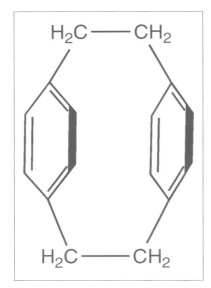

Why become interested in such a molecule? Its internal strain. The presence of the two bridges, each made of two mutually-bonded carbons, pulls on the benzene rings. Such double bridging tends to distort the benzene rings from their coplanarity. Would this, besides the geometry, affect the ability of the benzene rings to either accept or donate some of their electrons to another entity?

When Cram and Bauer did this work, chemists at the Central Experimental station, of DuPont de Nemours in Wilmington, Delaware had just made tetracyanoethylene (TCNE) in quantity (shown at bottom).

TCNE is a powerful attractor of electrons, because each CN group is polarized in the same manner as in HCN, with a positively-charged carbon. Moreover, TCNE is a planar molecule just like benzene.

Cram and Bauer thus studied the so-called charge-transfer complexes which occur when a paracyclophane comes together with a TCNE molecule. Such a complex is depicted below depicted in the top illustration on the next page.

The two benzene rings are in roughly planar and parallel vertical planes. The TCNE molecule, also in a vertical plane in this image, stacks next to one of the benzene rings,

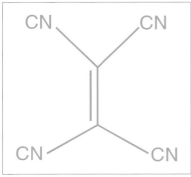

but on the outside (it is too bulky for the internal space of the paracyclophane).

An electronic interaction is thus set: the TCNE moiety (red) pulls electrons away from the paracyclophane moiety (blue). Each of the two benzene rings donates electrons, as shown by the horizontal arrows, which the TCNE avidly pulls:

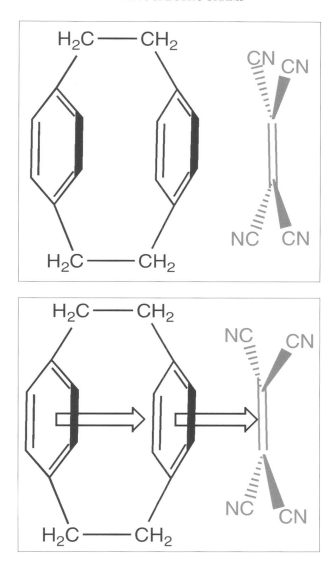

But we are moving too quickly: this last image already translates into the iconic language of *chemistry* the information latent in the very first image as provided by *spectroscopy*.

Extrapolating to a trend from discrete data points

At the time of the study by Cram and Bauer, the study of charge-transfer processes was in full bloom. A charge-transfer process occurs when, because of a sticky collision between two different molecules, electron density flows from one molecule to the other. Each curve in the spectrum results from such an event.

A relevant question, left unanswered by these spectra is that of the geometry of the collision complex: is it a sandwich-type, with the TCNE inserted in-between the two benzene rings; or is it an outer complex, with the TCNE positioned on top of one of the benzene rings? Spectroscopy of other sorts can help answer such questions.

Spectroscopy was devised in mid-nineteenth century by Bunsen (1811-1899) and Kirchhoff (1824-1887). Art influenced science. The very first mode of representation chosen by Bunsen was to depict a spectrum in silhouette manner; it looked like a mountain range, shown upside-down (1864):

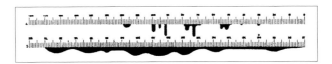

The lingering effect of this initial choice, now that spectra are shown as line drawings, is in the vocabulary, with its "peaks" and "valleys." Each of the eight curves in the first diagram on page 61 — each on a different paracyclophane — has two peaks. They document a gradual shift of one of the peaks toward longer wavelengths (toward the right in this graph). It turned out that the more basic the paracyclophane hydrocarbon (that is, the better it is at electron donation), the more electron pumping into TCNE occurs. The attendant charge-transfer band shifts to longer wavelengths.

Looking at that diagram, a chemist's eye immediately sees the trend for gradually greater basicity of the paracyclophanes. In an instat, then, a chemist can extrapolate from a set of separating pictures to a unifying hypothesis.

From simple to complex

This is the gist of this work, generalizing the notion of basicity (the converse of acidity) to these chemicals, called aromatic hydrocarbons. (And thus, to give it its technical explanation, to *pi* electrons instead of *n* electrons as is the case for traditional bases, such as nitrogen-containing molecules.) There is much more that spectroscopy can do with these molecules. The authors, Cram and Bauer, did not attempt to "deconvolute" each spectrum into its component absorptions. Thus it would be mistaken to equate the apparent absorption maxima (the red dots added to the figure) with the true maximum, as is often done. The "real" spectra are far more complex and spiky than these smooth curves suggest.

So spectroscopy is a signal example of a technology that began as a sensuous science, with all the colors of the rainbow, and gradually lost its visual content. We reproduce the one illustration from the 1950's experiment in a small size because it does not need to be any larger: it has no crucial visual details except the progression of peaks to the right. The Vreeland spectroscope is a survivor of the field's past. Today spectroscopic analyses do not even need to be given as graphs, although they often are. Numbers are all that is required in the end.

Resisting big science

More generally, spectroscopy is the handmaiden of chemistry. At the time when the work on paracyclophanes was carried out, research was on the rise on account of Vannevar Bush's report to the President of the United States, titled *Science: The Endless Frontier* (1945); chemistry laboratories were undergoing a qualitative and quantitative mutation. They were equipping themselves with extremely expensive commercial spectrometers. Within a few years, the cost of running a chemical laboratory increased between one and two orders of magnitude.

Chemists, who were following the lead set by physicists, were thus presented with the dilemma of embracing Big Science or sticking to their traditional, low-tech craft. For the most part, they opted for the latter. They went for the heavy equipment, but they managed to avoid it affecting the style of their research; chemistry continued to be done in small groups, with emphasis on manual dexterity, and on quick experiments which could be initiated in the morning and provide results in the afternoon. In a sense, spectroscopy retains the simple formats it once had.

For further reading

The report *Science: The Endless Frontier* is available at www.nsf.gov/od/lpa/nsf50/vbush1945.htm. For the early work on paracyclophanes, see D. J. Cram and S. H. Bauer's paper in the *Journal of the American Chemical Society* 81 (1959): 5971-77.

Photograph: B. Sweeney DTS, UCC, of Knitting Map Performance 1, Jools
Gilson-Ellis of Half/Angel 2004 (as part of Sweeney's ongoing research
project on documentation & performance)

PERFORUM

theatre space writing performance music light theory silence technology voice object dance sound video practice body text

**SPRING
'05**

2

How is Performance Documented?

Bernadette Sweeney

Performance is a notoriously ephemeral medium. Some artists make a virtue of that, but for others it presents a problem: how can a work whose meaning is in the making be preserved? The photos in this chapter record performances by the artist Jools Gilson-Ellis and others. In the nature of performance, these events varied hugely: one was a large outdoor event (held, as it happened, in a misting rain), and others were seen by fewer people.

The idea

Performance art, which has become increasingly important since its beginnings in the 1960s, continues to present difficult problems for historians and critics. Once the performance is over, what remains? Usually written descriptions, photographs, and sometimes also video.

Are those documents then the performance, as it will be known to future artists, historians, and critics? Or are they a kind of documentation that will always be inadequate? (And if so, how can we say how inadequate?)

Problems: the body

One crucial problem is that performance is about the body, and so it can never be put adequately into words. As Peggy Phelan has observed, performance moves from the "grammar of the word" to the "grammar of the body." How, then, to do that justice in videos and photographs? Two of these images document a knitting project, in which the artist worked with people in many different settings; part of those events was a closeness between people. Photographs can only capture that by reminding us of what it might have been like: a mnemonic prod, as much as a realistic record.

Problems: time

A second problem is that performance is a "time art": it cannot, by its nature, be documented in 2-D or 3-D. W.B. Worthen has noted that "all writing about performance must face its own impossibility: the event is gone, [and] the records are always partial and suspect."

It is a difficult starting-point for any documentary project. In one photo at the top of the previous page, a man is slightly out of focus, giving a sense of his motion; in the photo below, two figures move across a dark field and are intentionally blurred to evoke their gestures and speed. In such ways photography translates bodily motions, and our perceptions of them, into conventional equivalents.

The uniqueness of performance art

Recently, Phelan and others have proposed that performance art is unique exactly because it cannot be documented. Irit Rogoff and Gavin Butt at Goldsmith's in London have suggested that an entirely new kind of writing needs to be developed to adequately respond to performance. It is not enough, they say, to simply describe or document: the critic or historian has to enact the performance through writing. Journals like *Performance Research* and books such as *ReMembering the Body* try to embrace the new ideals.

In this way of thinking, performance demands not only sensitive and thorough documentation, but a new kind of documentation. The practice reflected in these documents is one of questioning: I ask about the relationship between the languages of the script, the stage, and the critic, and about what happens during the performance moment when "the word" is made flesh — or, in the end, what then happens when the performance is critiqued and the "flesh" is made word.

The place of the visual

Visual documentation, whether it is video or photography, brings with it an ideology and an aesthetic which prevent it from functioning simply as evidence. The visual becomes suspect: it is no longer evidential, but contentious. That is true, in varying degrees, of every image in this book: but here it can be perceived as a crippling defect. Performance art is, in this sense, immune from the danger of being reduced to documentary evidence.

For further reading

After Criticism: New Responses to Art and Performance, edited by Gavin Butt (Maiden MA: Blackwell, 2005); Peggy Phelan, *Unmarked: the Politics of Performance* (New York: Routledge, 1993), quotation on p. 150; *ReMembering the Body,* edited by Gabrielle Brandstetter and Hortensia Völckers, with contributions by Bruce Mau and André Lepecki (Ostfildern-Ruit: Hatje Cantz, 2000) (I thank Michelle Tupko for this reference – J.E.); W.B. Worthen, *Theorizing Practice: Redefining Theatre History* (New York: Palgrave Macmillan, 2003), quotation on p. 6; and Bernadette Sweeney, "Wordmadeflesh: Writing the Body in Irish Theatre," *Modern Drama* 47 no. 4 (2004), quotations on p. 686.

3

Deductions from Smooth Rocks
Bettie Higgs

Most of the rocks in this photograph are about 360 million years old, so the grains that comprise them are substantially older.

The grains came originally from a mountain range, as large as the Himalayas, whose roots can still be seen in counties Mayo and Donegal, in the northwest of Ireland. The grains were carried south by rivers and deposited in this area; the smallest grains were carried all the way to the ocean, which was far south of Cork at the time, in what is now the Atlantic Ocean south of Ireland. (There was very little rainfall at the time: the portion of land that is now Cork was 10° south of the Equator. This can be deduced from the properties of the iron in the rock.)

The water in which the grains were transported was oxygenated, and the iron precipitated out as iron oxide (hematite), which cemented the grains and which accounts for the red color.

Aeons underground

The grains were buried by overlying sediment, forming fine layers. (They can be seen in the photo on the next page.) As the grains were cemented into rock, and the layers built up, the sea encroached from the south. The sea slowly flooded the land, and for a time it was nearly 1000m deep in this area. These rocks were several kilometres beneath the ocean floor.

Then the layers were uplifted, and folded, forming the Variscan mountains. The remains of these mountains are seen today throughout counties Cork and Kerry, in the west and southwest of Ireland. Once again the area subsided under the sea (between 200 million and 100 million years ago). More sediment accumulated — this time chalk.

Then, during the past 60 million years, the strata uplifted again, as a distant part of the Alpine mountain building event. The layers on top eroded away; and in the last 1 million years glaciers scoured off still more layers. Eventually, the rocks you see now were exposed.

The pieces the glacier scoured were sharp and angular. These rocks were rounded by glacial melt water and by ocean waves during the last 10,000 years.

Shape of grains

The same reasoning can be applied to the grains in the rock, which are from mountains and strata older than 360 million years. Through a magnifying glass it is possible to discern some angular grains and some rounded ones. A microscope shows the shapes even more clearly (see the photo on the next page).

Differential wear

The shape of grains depends on the nature of the mineral: some grains in the rocks are made of quartz and so are relatively hard and resistant to weathering. This quartz is white or colorless, and has a glassy appearance. Other grains are composed of softer minerals, such as mica, which wear more quickly. Mica is visible as silvery flakes in the rocks.

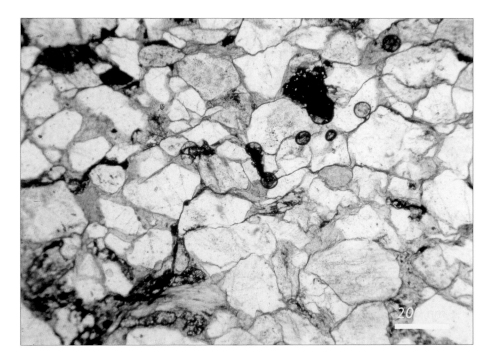

How much can be told by shape?

There is a limit to how useful this is. Some of these rocks are comprised of materials which are harder and wear more slowly than others. The pink crystalling rock at the right in the opening photograph was actually a "grain" in a 360 million year old sediment. The rounding to give the rock this almost spherical shape took place before this time. Here the layers — seen close-up on the next page — are not sedimentary layers. Heat and pressure has caused the separation into bands of quartz and pink feldspars, and dark colored micas and amphiboles.

Another limiting factor is that the rocks become rounded more quickly in quick-flowing streams, and more slowly in lakes where the water current is less energetic.

Likewise some grains are very round — nearly perfect spheres — but that does not mean they are the oldest. By looking at the shape of the grains within the rock geologists can tell if the grains were transported by water or by wind. Windblown quartz grains are perfectly rounded, and have a matt surface texture. Grains transported by water are not so well rounded and have a glassy surface texture.

This is the beginning of the analysis. There are many more factors to consider, including the composition of the grains, and the heat and pressure to which they

were subjected when they were buried. Those factors are part of Pat Meere's study, Chapter 23.

For further reading

Ivor Mccarthy and Pat Meere, *Geology of the Devonian-Carboniferous South Munster Basin, Ireland* (Cork: Department Of Geology Report, UCC, 2004); A.G. Sleeman and M. Pracht, *Geology of South Cork* (Dublin: Geological Survey of Ireland, 1994); Raymond Siever, *Sand* (New York: Scientific American Library, 1988); F. J. Pettijohn, P. E. Potter, and R. Siever, *Sand and Sandstone,* second edition (New York: Springer-Verlag, 1987); and Elkins, *How to Use Your Eyes* (New York: Routledge, 2000), chapter 23, "How to Look at Sand."

CONSTITUTIONAL POLITICAL ECONOMY

Vol. 2, No. 2   Spring/Summer 1991

14 AUG 1991

ARTICLES

REVIEWS

Editors: Viktor J. Vanberg
            Richard E. Wagner

Center for Study of Public Choice

George Mason University

4

A Wandering Image of the Sirens

Brendan McElroy, John Considine and James Elkins

The picture on the cover of this journal is Odysseus, tied to the mast of his ship, listening to the song of the Sirens: a familiar image, but an unexpected icon for this journal. The familiar story comes from the *Odyssey:*

> First you'll approach the Sirens, who charm all
> Men who come near them. He who witlessly
> Draws near and listens to the Sirens' voice
> His wife and infant children never shall
> Stand joyful by, when he comes home. Instead
> The Sirens with their shrill song shall him charm.
> They sit in pastures. Yet around them lies
> A heap of rotting men, mere skin and bone.
> Drive past this place, but first knead honeyed wax
> And stop your comrades' ears, lest any hear.
> But if you wish yourself to hear their song,
> Have your men tie you up both hand and foot
> Upon the swift ship's mast-box, standing up,
> With cables lashed around, so that you may
> Delight in listening to the Sirens' song.
> But if you beg your comrades and demand
> Release, they are to bind you closer still.

> — Homer, *Odyssey* 12.39–54: *The Sirens*, newly translated by Keith Sidwell

The sirens in economic theory

Two economists at the University College Cork, Brendan McElroy and John Considine, were interested in the fact that this journal has taken the picture of Odysseus and the Sirens as an emblem of what is called in economics the *time inconsistency problem.* This arises when it is known that the incentives facing

individuals will change due to the passage of time, making it unlikely that they
will carry out plans that benefit all participants. The journal of *Constitutional
Political Economy* uses the image of the Sirens to illustrate the use of binding
rules to overcome the time inconsistency problem. Here is how the editors of
the journal explain it in the journal's inaugural issue:

> [*Constitutional Political Economy's*] logo is a representation of the familiar Homeric
> account of how Ulysses heard the Sirens' singing, and survived. By exploiting ele-
> ments of his natural and social environment, Ulysses was able to subvert certain in-
> clinations of his future self, inclinations that he knew would be destructive of his
> overall interests but which would nevertheless prove irresistible when they arose.
> Ulysses imagined the alternative possible futures; he isolated the best for himself; but
> he required the technology of mast and rope to secure the best possible future. He
> established for himself a private constitution, a set of more or less binding rules that
> constrain his future choices (Brennan and Kliemt, 1990, 125).

The time inconsistency problem in more detail

The less than perfect enforcement of contract in some third world countries, for
example, results in the majority of markets in these countries being *spot markets,*
where both sides of a transaction fulfil their obligations on the spot. Similarly, a
government may seek to balance the public sector budget over the business cycle,
running a deficit to stimulate the economy during recessions and keeping a surplus during boom times. However, the temptation to spend the surplus or cut
taxes during boom times may prove too great, leading to a fiscal policy that has
a destabilizing effect on the business cycle, with excessive booms and deeper
recessions.

The inability of individuals to commit to a course of action means that many
potentially beneficial economic exchanges are not consummated. To avoid such
a problem there is a need to provide a commitment mechanism such as enforce-
able rules and laws.

The time inconsistency problem arises in many areas of Economics including
investment decisions in developing countries and budgetary policy. Many entrepreneurs do not undertake potentially profitable investments in developing
countries because the less than perfect enforcement of contract law means that
they cannot get a credible commitment from other entrepreneurs in these countries. Would you produce and deliver goods if you knew that if payment is not
received, the contract may be unenforceable?

Budgetary policy provides another example of the benefit of rules. A government working in the public's interest would attempt to balance the public sector
budget over the business cycle, running a deficit to stimulate the economy during
recessions and keeping a surplus during boom times to balance things up. However, the temptation to spend the surplus or cut taxes during boom times may

prove too great, leading to budgetary policy having a destabilizing effect on the business cycle, with excessive booms and deeper recessions. To prevent governments from succumbing to this temptation, some economists believe that governments should be bound by the constitution to balance their budget. Indeed, the E.U.'s Growth and Stability Pact is a variant of such a rule.

The sirens in the history of art

So: the image seems appropriate for *Constitutional Political Economy,* but there are other dimensions to the image that have — apparently — little to do with economics.

In the history of art, the image of the Sirens has been used for many purposes. They have represented licentiousness and "animal appetites." They have been taken as emblems of the *femme fatale,* and they were popular in turn-of-the-century decadent art. In the late nineteenth century, they represented Oriental culture (even though they were Greek).

The sirens in philosophy

And there is still more to the story of the Sirens: it has also been used in Anglo-American philosophy, as an emblem of the problem of *akrasia,* weakness of will: a philosophic problem wholly unrelated to the time inconsistency problem or to the moralizing uses of the past. In this way the history of images continues on its uneven way.

What's strange about this

In the history of art, images are usually thought of as having continuous histories: a picture like this might be used to make an ethical point, then a moral one, then a sexual one — all the meanings flow into one another, growing organically as cultures and communities change. The study of such meanings is part of iconography.

But in recent art history, scholars have been paying more attention to images that don't behave so well: their meanings jump and shift unpredictably. Historians such as Georges Didi-Huberman have pointed out how images can resurface at unexpected times and places, and with unpredictable functions. The result is a kind of psychoanalysis of culture rather than a historiography. Images have lives that go well beyond their intended uses, and beyond the disciplines that may want to own them. (In the United States, Ajax, a great hero of the *Iliad,* lives on as a laundry detergent.) Even an image from the journal *Constitutional Political Economy* can make its way into a history of images that is open to wider models of influence. The time inconsitency problem is just one episode in the history of images of the Sirens, and the methodology that might link it to its other appearances in art and in philosophy has get to be invented.

For further reading

G. Brennan and H. Kliemt, "Logo Logic," *Constitutional Political Economy* 1 no. 1 (1990): 125-27; J. Buchanan and G. Tullock, *The Calculus of Consent* (Ann Arbor, MI: University of Michigan Press, 1962); G. Brennan and J. Buchanan, *The Power to Tax* (Indianapolis, IN: Liberty Press, 2000); Jean Seznec, *The Survival of the Pagan Gods: The Mythological Tradition and Its Place in Renaissance Humanism and Art* (Princeton, NJ: Princeton University Press, 1953); and Georges Didi-Huberman, *l'Image survivante, Histoire de l'art et temps des fantômes selon Aby Warburg* (Paris: Minuit, 2002). The "logo" was also noticed by Hartmut Kliemt of the University of Duisburg-Essen, in an essay called "The Rationality of Rational Fools: The Role of Commitments, Persons and Agents in Rational Choice Modeling" (available on the university's website, accessed August 2006).

5

Color Terms in Medieval Ireland

Caitríona Ó Dochartaigh and John Carey

Some languages have hundreds of words for colors; others have just a few. According to one linguist, the normal number of "basic" color terms in any language is eleven: beyond that the color terms are dependent on particular references ("peach," "lavender," "Payne's gray").

There are three variables in color names: their forms in different languages ("red," "Rot," "rouge"); what they denote (reflectances, spectra); and the concepts that supposedly order them ("primaries," "color wheels"). According to some theories, color names evolve principally when there is a need: people coin them and adapt them in response to their environment. Another theory is that the evolution of color terms is governed as much by linguistic rules as it is by perceptual constraints.

In our field of medieval Irish studies, color theory remains largely unexplored, and many intriguing questions remain open. For instance, the Irish (and Welsh) adjective *glas* can refer to the colors which we call "blue," "green" and "grey"; how were these colors perceived by people who made no verbal distinction between them? According to the color theorists Brent Berlin and Paul Kay, languages which do not make this distinction stand at a relatively early point in the development of a color vocabulary: but how do we square this with the passionate love of color which is so obvious in medieval Irish art and literature?

The Book of Ballymote *and Ogam script*

The manuscript illustrated here is in the Royal Irish Academy in Dublin. It was written around 1400 in the town of Ballymote, in County Sligo in northwest Ireland, under the patronage of a family named MacDonagh, by various hands. Much of the content of the *Book of Ballymote* consists of Gaelic historical, legendary and genealogical material, as well as translations of classical works, but it also includes a unique grammatical treatise entitled *Auraicept na n-Éces* or "The Scholars' Primer." *Auraicept na n-Éces* is the first attempt at a systematic analysis of the structure and grammar of the Irish language and is one of the earliest European vernacular grammars in any language. The author was interested in many aspects of the Irish language, including the Ogam alphabet.

Ogam (pronounced AWG-am or OH-am; spelled Ogham or Ogam) is a script whose letters take the form of lines, like hatchmarks. The earliest Ogam takes the form of notches carved in standing stones; it is known as Orthodox Ogam. This early alphabet used a series of twenty characters arranged in four groups. The first photo is a standing stone in Ireland, marked with Orthodox Ogam; the inscriptions are usually names.

There is another, later type of Ogam, usually referred to as Scholastic Ogam, which is found in medieval manuscripts. This later form takes Orthodox Ogam as a starting point and develops many variations of the alphabet.

The author of *Auraicept na n-Éces* was particularly interested in the classification system of Orthodox Ogam: the different sets of names for the Ogam letters, which are arranged in four groups of five characters. These four groups in the Ogam alphabet are identified by the first letter of each group: B, H, M, A. In *Auraicept na n-Éces* the author was so taken with this classification system that he tried to group many other things, in no way connected with sound, under the letter headings. This resulted in groups which he labeled with titles such as "King Ogam." "Boy Ogam," "Water Ogam," "Cow Ogam," and "Sow Ogam." The page illustrated here has a number of such schemes. One paragraph in particular concerns visual metaphors for Ogam letters (in the red rectangle).

"Color Ogam"

What we are interested in here is "Color Ogam"; it is of particular significance to those researching the history of color classification and terminology. The final illustration here is a detail of the "Color Ogam" passage. Below it is a transcription, in traditional Irish font, followed by the same in a modern font, and finally a translation. The groups are groups of letters in the Ogam alphabet, so the author is saying that one letter, like "A" in our alphabet, symbolizes "white," and another, say "B," symbolizes "grey," and so forth.

The inaccessibility of past color worlds

What, then, was the color experience of this writer? Are these color-terms meant to convey the range of his perceptions?

Why did he group certain colors together? Some of these color words are familiar in modern Irish, but the history of color terms warns us not to conclude that if the scribe who wrote this were here, he would agree with us on the identification of any of the colors.

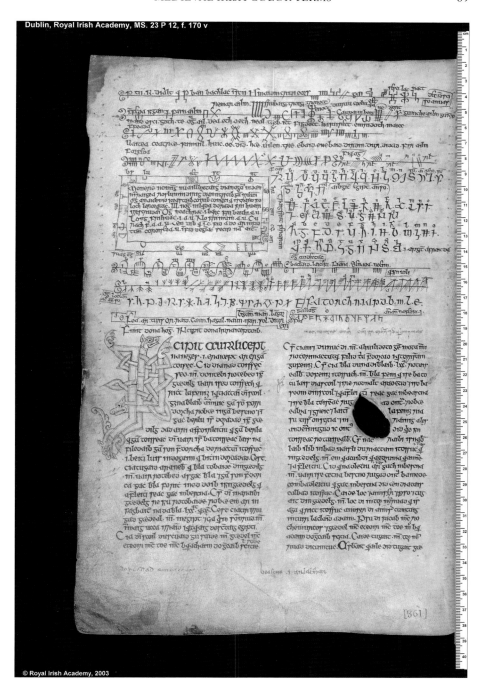

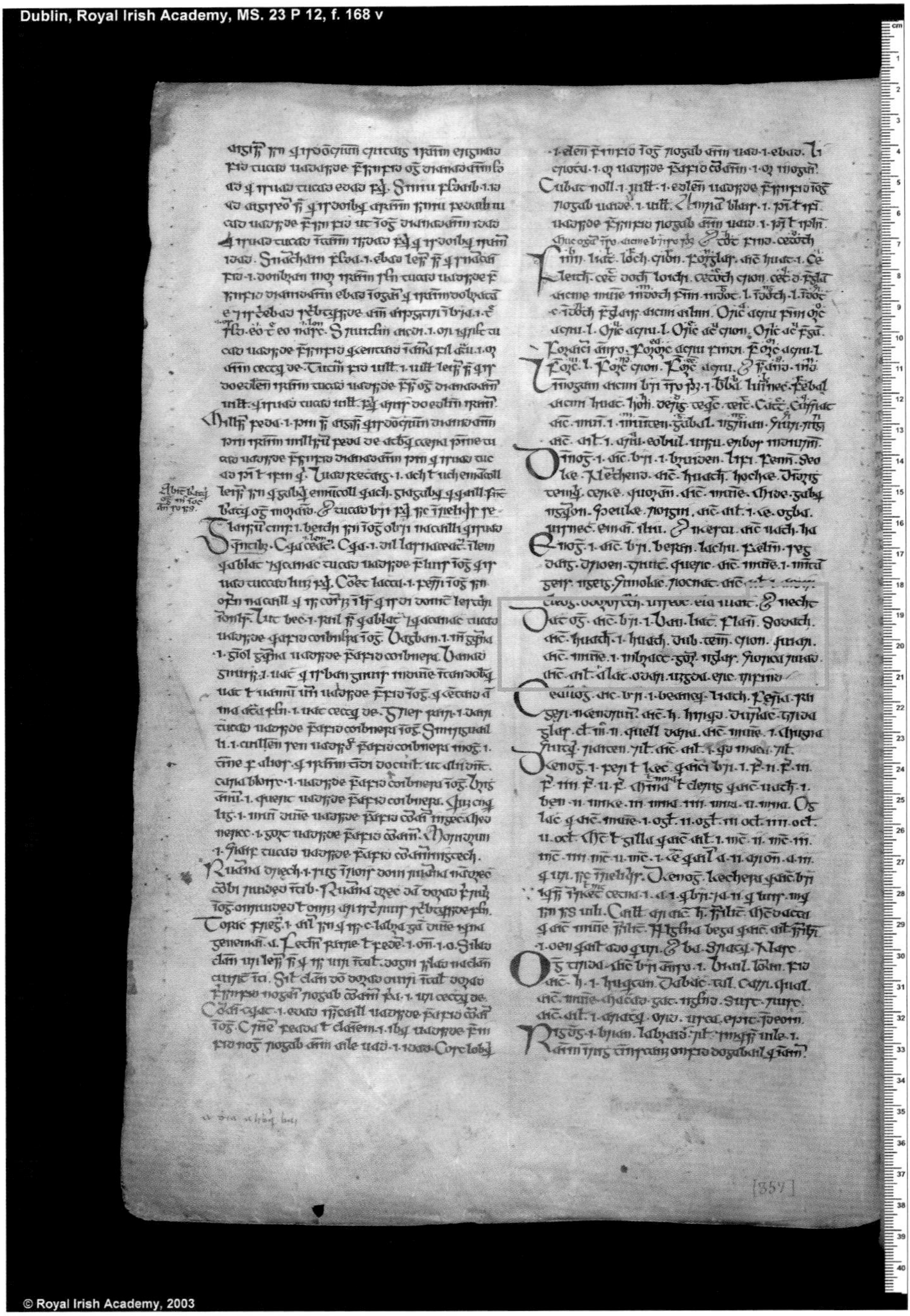
Dublin, Royal Irish Academy, MS. 23 P 12, f. 168 v
© Royal Irish Academy, 2003

Ɒᴀᴄʜoᴣᴀɴ. ᴀɪcᴍe ʙeᴄʜɪ .ɪ. ʙᴀɴ, Lɪᴀᴄʜ, ꜰLᴀɴɴ, soᴅᴀᴄʜ, ɴecʜᴄ.
    ᴀɪcᴍe ʜᴜᴀᴄʜᴀ .ɪ. ʜᴜᴀᴄʜ, ᴅᴜʙ, ᴄeᴍeɴ, cʀoɴ, qᴜɪᴀʀ.
    ᴀɪcᴍe ᴍᴜɪɴe .ɪ. ᴍʙʀᴀcʜᴄ, ᴣoʀᴍ, ɴᴣLᴀs, sʀoʀcᴀ, ʀᴜᴀᴅʜ.
    ᴀɪcᴍe ᴀɪLᴍe: ᴀLᴀᴄʜ, oᴅʜᴀʀ, ᴜsᴣᴅʜᴀ, eʀc, ɪʀꜰɪɴᴅ.

Dathogam. Aicme bethi .i. ban, liath, flann, sodath, necht.
    Aicme huatha .i. huath, dub, temen, cron, quiar.
    Aicme muine .i. mbracht, gorm, nglas, srorca, ruadh.
    Aicme ailme: alath, odhar, usgdha, erc, irfind.

Colour Ogam. Group B, i.e., white, grey, blood-red, fine-coloured, clear.
    Group H, i.e., earth-coloured, black, dark, brown, jet.
    Group M, i.e., variegated, deep-blue, light-green/blue, bright, brownish-red.
    Group A. piebald, dun, resin-coloured, speckled, very white.

Other terms are unfamiliar, and some would not be thought of as a color at all. (What color is "speckled"?) The conceptual problem of re-imagining words into visual phenomena is even more intractable here than it is in, say, contemporary color science, where at least the problems can be quantified. In this case, color is entangled in language, culture and history.

A hidden motive

This example shows just how difficult, how tricky, it can be to try to understand other people's color perceptions. It also shows how odd the history of Ogam script is, from inscribed stones — studied in Chapter 22 — to elaborate and eccentric symbolic schemata. But there is another message here as well: this is the length to which we have to go if we want to enlist medieval Irish as a "visual" discipline. Some fields are just intrinsically non-visual, or resistant to visual meaning, and that recalcitrance has to be taken seriously in any project of analyzing visuality.

For further reading

The manuscript can be seen in all its 100MB splendor on www.isos.dias.ie (Royal Irish Academy: MS 23 P 12, ff. 168v, 169r, 169v). Information on Orthodox Ogam: Damian McManus, *The Ogam Stones at University College Cork* (Cork: Cork University Press, 2004); Francesco Benozzo, *Landscape Perception in Early Celtic Literatures* (Aberystwyth: Celtic Studies Publications, 2003); James Elkins, *The Domain of Images* (Ithaca NY: Cornell University Press, 1999). For Scholarly Ogham see: Heidi Lazar-Meyn, "Color Terms in *Táin Bó Cúailnge*", in *Ulidia*, edited by J.P. Mallory and Gerard Stockman (Belfast: December Publications, 1994), 201-205; George Calder, *Auraicept na n-Éces: The Scholars" Primer* (Edinburgh: John Grant, 1917). General background on medieval Irish color perception: John Carey, "Cosmology in *Saltair na Rann*", *Celtica* 17 (1985), pp. 33-52; Clare Stancliffe, "Red, white and blue martyrdom" in *Ireland in Early Mediaeval Europe*, edited by Dorothy Whitelock et al. (Cambridge: Cambridge University Press, 1982). Good introductory sources for color philosophy and science: *Color: Art and Science*, edited by Trevor Lamb and Janine Bourriau (Cambridge: Cambridge University Press, 1995); John Gage, *Color and Culture: Practice and Meaning from Antiquity to Abstraction* (London: Thames & Hudson, 1993); Hazel Rossotti, *Color: Why the World Isn't Grey* (Princeton NJ: Princeton University Press, 1983); Berlin Kay, *Basic Color Terms: Their Universality and Evolution* (Berkeley: University of California Press, 1969).

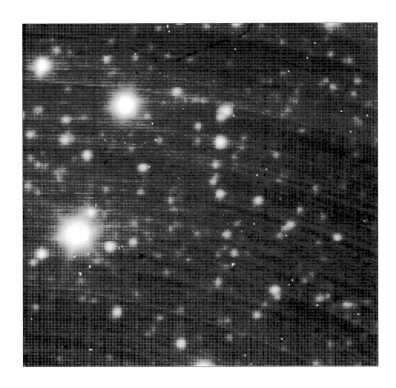

6

Doppler Tomography of Accretion Disks: Ultrahigh-Resolution Astronomy

Paul Callanan

One of the many achievements of astronomy over the last few decades has been to greatly improve the detail in astronomical images. This has occurred right across the electromagnetic spectrum — in radio, optical and even X-ray wavelengths.

High resolution radio images are accomplished by the techniques of interferometry. The best optical images are obtained using similar techniques from the ground, or by direct imaging from space. Even in the X-ray, the finely polished mirrors of the Chandra X-ray observatory (with surfaces fashioned to an accuracy of a few atomic diameters) generate images of comparable detail to those obtained optically from the ground.

Despite these advances, it remains very difficult to resolve the disk of a star, or of a planet orbiting another star. If astronomical image-making were possible with even higher resolution, then the door would be open to the study of many new phenomena.

Two-dimensional stars

A relatively new technique has been developed to study a particular type of astronomical object, found in many parts of our Galaxy (and others).

Disks of gas are known to orbit many different types of stars. For example, a residue of material orbited the "proto-sun," before it settled down to life as a normal star. This material was initially in the form of a disk, from which the planets eventually formed. Such disks are observed around other young stars today.

Many binary star systems in our Galaxy also harbor such disks. In these systems, a neutron star, white dwarf or black hole orbits a companion star. The binary is so "tight" that material is accreted from the companion star to the compact object, forming a disk as it does so. This "accretion disk" is heated by the viscous interaction of the gas and any irradiation from the compact object (often a highly luminous emitter of X-rays). It appears almost like a two-dimensional star, with a temperature that increases dramatically towards it center.

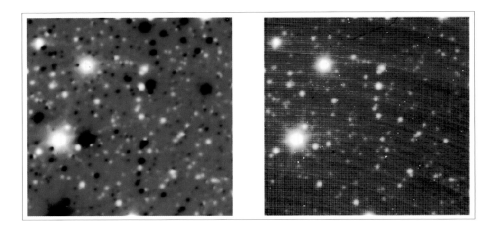

Indirect imaging of accretion disks

At first sight, the idea of studying the structure of such disks seems technically impossible. A disk comparable in size to the sun even at a moderate distace would require an angular resolution of a few millionths of a second of arc: that is 100 to 1,000 times smaller than the best resolution radio or optical observations can offer. Here, a candidate system is shown, but the phenomena that require study are nearly beyond the limit of the telescope.

However, many of these accretion disks are in binaries with relatively short orbital periods (several hours to days). Hence, we get to see various aspects of the accretion disk projected along our line of sight, and this allows us to construct maps of the accretion disk, in a way similar to that used in X-ray Computer Aided Tomography (CAT) scans. Indeed, the technique is called Doppler tomography of accretion disks.

In a CAT scan, X-rays are passed through a plane of the body from many different angles, and an image is obtained for each. These images can be combined using the "maximum entropy method" (MEM) to produce a reliable 2-D image of the X-ray absorption within the body.

In the case of a binary star, the system itself rotates for us. Hence we can observe the spectrum of the accretion disk from many lines of sight. This spectrum contains many emission lines; the structure and location of such lines provides us with information about the speed of the material from which they came. A

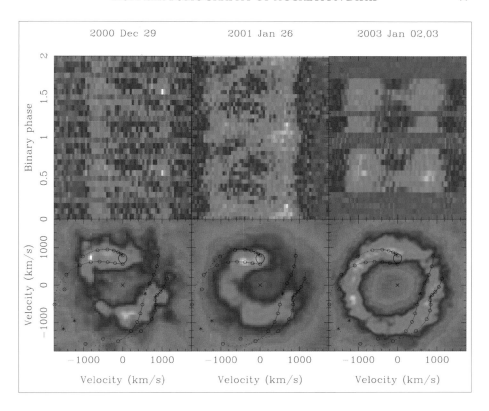

line with a laboratory wavelength of λ_0, say, is shifted to either longer wavelengths (to the red) or shorter wavelengths (to the blue) depending on whether the gas emitting the line is travelling towards or away from us. This is called the Doppler effect. (See Chapter 12 for another example.)

Spectrograms and Doppler images

Hence, these line profiles give information about the velocity of the gas in the disk, and from the variation of these profiles over the orbital phase we can create a map of the intensity distribution over the accretion disk — not in normal space but "velocity space".

The object here is the binary system with "black hole candidate" (a suspected black hole), numbered XTE J1118+480.

The top images here are "trailed" spectra of Hα emissions.

They are used to make "MEM Doppler maps," bottom, which record the position of the stars in the binary system in "velocity space": notice that both axes record velocity, and not position.

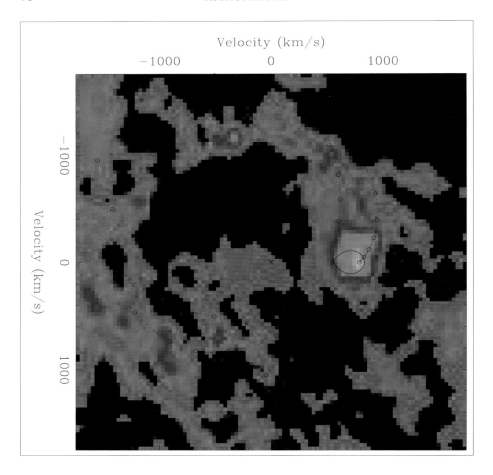

The result

By subtracting out symmetrical elements, it is possible to visualize emission concentrated toward the expected position of the secondary star of the pair.

The gas stream between the stars is the lower curve; the upper curve is the Keplerian disk along the stream; and the cross is the center of mass of the entire system.

If the material obeys Kepler's Laws as it orbits in the disk, then we can use the relationship between the gas velocity and its distance from the centre of the disk to generate, in theory, a map of the disk in real space.

As indirect as this technique is, it allows us to study phenomena that are otherwise completely inaccessible using other means.

For further reading

M.A.P. Torres, Paul Callanan et al., "MMT Observations Of The Black Hole Candidate XTE J1118+480 Near And In Quiescence," preprint at arXiv:astro-ph/0405509 (May 26, 2004).

M-0054-0021

24 GLENFADA PARK NORTH

7

The Bloody Sunday Tribunal Video Simulation

Darius Whelan

On Sunday, the 30th of January 1972, thirteen people were killed by British soldiers on the streets of Derry. The circumstances in which they died have been the subject of enormous on ongoing controversy. At the time, the British Army said that the soldiers had been firing at nail-bombers and gunmen. Many witnesses disagreed strongly, arguing that none of the shootings were justified because all of the victims had been unarmed civilians. A report was issued in the same year by the Widgery Tribunal; it found that there had been "no general breakdown in discipline" on the part of the soldiers, although

some of the firing "bordered on the reckless." The coroner, reporting in 1973, concluded very differently that "it was sheer, unadulterated murder." In 1998, a new Tribunal was established to reassess the facts and provide a new report (photo at right). This Tribunal, chaired by Lord Saville, heard evidence for a number of years and is preparing its report as of this writing (winter 2006).

An interactive virtual reality system was developed specifically for use by the Bloody Sunday Tribunal in order to aid the orientation of witnesses when they gave their evidence. The system consisted of thousands of photographs and computer-generated images of Derry, both present-day and as it was in 1972.

A combination of this application and touch-screen technology used in the hearing chamber allowed users to virtually walk the streets of Derry. Once a witness was viewing a particular "hotspot," he or she could view the scene from all angles. Witnesses could also draw arrows on the screen to record movements or events which they saw.

A sample piece of evidence using the virtual reality system

Ms. Nell McCafferty, a journalist, gave evidence that she witnessed certain events at a rubble barricade, including bodies being put into a jeep by soldiers (see the photo at the opening of this chapter). Mr. Christopher Clarke, QC, displayed a hotspot on screen and drew a blue arrow to indicate the line of sight she would have had from the window of a house in which she was located.

Following the line of sight indicated by the arrow, Mr. Clarke stated that Ms. McCafferty would have had a view of the rubble barricade. Earlier, another barrister, Lord Gifford, QC, had commented that as the house was slightly raised above the level of the ground, Ms. McCafferty would, when looking out of this window, have been able to see over the top of the fence.

A second piece of evidence

When Mr Denis Bradley (formerly Father Bradley) was called as a witness, he was shown certain hotspots on the screen and asked to point out exactly where he had observed a soldier standing when certain shots were fired. He marked the screen with various arrows. Then a barrister asked Mr Bradley the following question:

"The arrows show — the mauve arrow is where the people have been, the turquoise arrow is the route the soldiers came down, the green arrow is where the people were being taken by the soldiers back up into Glenfada Park North, the light blue arrow is approximately where the soldier was and the dark blue arrow is the direction into which he moved; is that right?"

Mr Bradley answered: "That is roughly correct."

The significance of the Virtual Reality system

In the earlier Widgery Tribunal hearings, extensive use had been made of maps, photographs and an architectural model of the area. The current Bloody Sunday Tribunal has vastly increased the amount of visual material available. The idea of bringing all of that information together into a virtual reality reconstruction (and including new images where necessary) proved to be of great assistance to the lawyers and witnesses trying to make sense of the complex events which occurred decades previously. Continuous reference was made to the photographs and maps, as well as the virtual reality recreation of 1972 Derry, especially as some buildings had been demolished since 1972.

Generally speaking, witnesses seemed to be quite comfortable with the virtual reality system, although it naturally took a few minutes for each witness to become familiar with this rather unusual means of representing the scenes. Witnesses quite often controlled the system, exploring the virtual space. Some witnesses corrected earlier statements based on what they saw on the virtual reality. For example, Mr Trevor McBride commented:

> Yes, if you can turn right, if I could put it like that again and maybe keep going right. I think just keep going right on. Now, if you could just stop there. I thought that I left the Shiels's home and came along this pathway, but I, I would not have been able to look to my right to have seen people lying at Abbey Park. So I think that the only route that makes any sense is coming down from Abbey Street down this little pathway where the tree is and then have glanced over to my right and have been aware of the people lying just where the car is, to the left of the car.

For the lawyers involved in the Tribunal, it was vital to be able to analyze the visual evidence in detail. It would not have been possible for a lawyer to participate in the Tribunal without studying maps, photographs, videotapes, and the virtual reality system in advance and being prepared to use those tools to clarify what witnesses were saying.

The Virtual Reality system made it possible to pose questions and to test witnesses' memories in a way that would not have been possible with photographs and maps. The Tribunal report is anticipated as this book goes to press; it will be interesting to see how the findings depend on the visual evidence and how it was deployed.

For further reading:

Bloody Sunday Tribunal website: www.bloody-sunday-inquiry.org.uk; British Irish Rights Watch Bloody Sunday Inquiry Reports: www.birw.org/bsireports/bsione.html; evidence of Nell McCafferty: Tribunal Transcript, Days 168 and 169; evidence of Denis Bradley: Day 140; evidence of Trevor McBride: Day 168. See further D. Mullan and J. Scally, *Eyewitness Bloody Sunday*, third edition (Dublin: Merlin, 2002); CAIN Web Service Bloody Sunday site: http://cain.ulst.ac.uk/events/bsunday/; UCR/California Museum of Photography Exhibition "Hidden Truths: Bloody Sunday 1972," January-March 2000: www.cmp.ucr.edu/photography/hidden/.

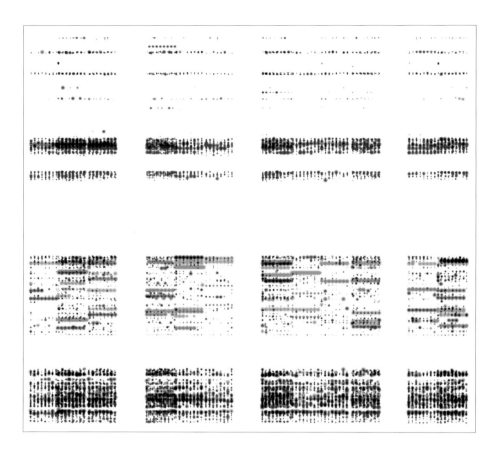

8

Maps of a University Computer Science Network, and the Internet

David O'Byrne and James Elkins

Nagios is software that monitors the status of computer servers; it is used for example in the Department of Computer Science at the University College Cork to watch the university's intranet. David O'Byrne has a copy of Nagios on his desktop computer, and he keeps an eye on the university intranet with the help of an icon in lower-right-hand corner of his screen.

When the Nagios icon is a green, all is well. If something is a slightly wrong, a yellow icon shows up; a more serious problem, and the icon turns red. This simple scheme means critical IT equipment cannot "die quietly" and saves the Computer Science IT staff from having to continuously check the status of the servers.

Pictures of the UCC network

Once a problem is indicated, Nagios offers have choice of more detailed representations. There is a 3-D status map (top photo on the next page), but it does not give much information without zooming — notice the labels are illegible onscreen. The image shows a representation of the computer that has the Nagios software on it (the Large "Nagios" box) and a representation of the network links (lines) and Computer Science Server Computers (the green and red boxes). (In all these representations, the names of the servers have been changed for security reasons.)

Nagios also offers a 2-D status map (bottom photo on the next page). Here it is clear that connections between the net router (a server that communicates with the internet) are down, and also that the university firewall is not operative.

The non-graphical interface

IT staff prefer a non-graphical option: the tabular report called Host Detail (top foto on the second page following). It gives the most information, showing when the servers became inaccessible. Each server is listed. If the background is green, all is well for that server. If it is red, a problem has been encountered by the Nagios software. Further detail on what the problem was, and what time it was encountered are listed next to each server.

This is an instance of the limitations of images, because the 3-D view cannot provide the information that the tabular view can. But note that the missing information is not itself pictorial: what is missing is alphanumeric. It's a different question whether the 3-D representation *itself* conveys sufficient information to be useful. At UCC, at least, it does not.

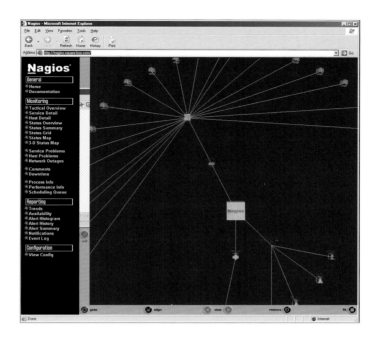

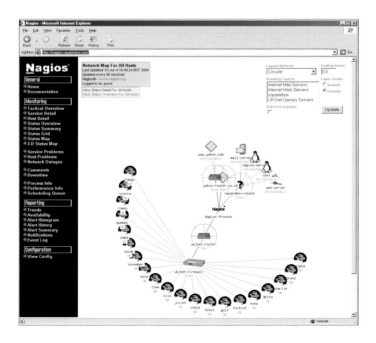

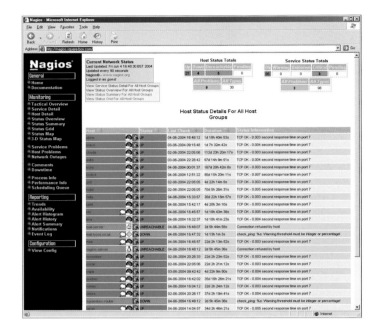

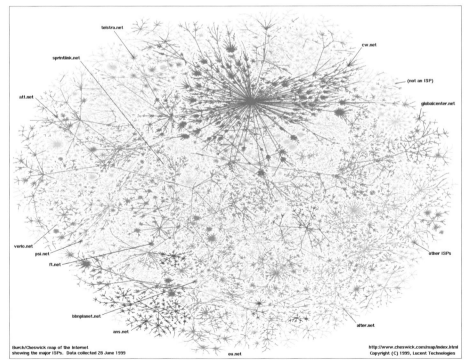

Burch/Cheswick map of the Internet
showing the major ISPs. Data collected 28 June 1999

http://www.cheswick.com/map/index.html
Copyright (C) 1999, Lucent Technologies

Other graphical representations

There have been many attempts to show the internet, and parts of it, as flowcharts and other 3-D and 2-D graphics. An online *Atlas of Cyberspaces* samples the possibilities, and the online journal *Mappa mundi* has published other kinds of maps. Most famously, Hal Burch and Bill Cheswick made a map of the entire internet that was featured in *Wired* magazine, showing the relative sizes of the principal internet domains (see the bottom photo on the previous page). There are a number of versions of this map, customized to showcase individual companies.

Artistic representations

In the world of internet art, there is also Lisa Jevbratt's work called *Migration: Interface 1,* which maps IP addresses in several different ways. This image is a map of the internet in 1999 (red), 2001 (green), and 2005 (purple), with each pixel representing 255 IP addresses. The image on the next page is a detail, with some IP addresses visible.

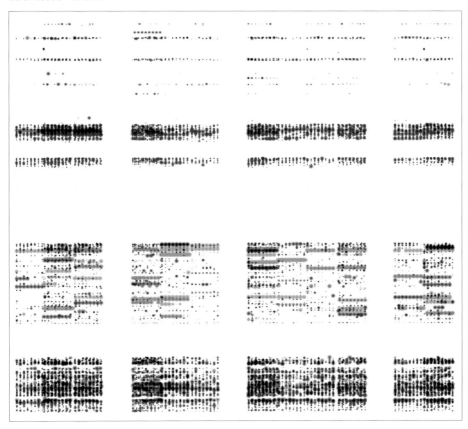

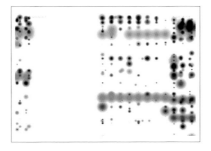

The image below is another of Jevbratt's maps of the internet showing all sites, in those same years (above and below). The colors are determined by the four parts of the IP address (eg., 0.0.0.0).

Try this at home

Any PC can run the software called Visualware, which traces the routes by which emails arrive, or by which your server finds another, and gives both graphical and tabular results. In the example shown on the next page, a web browser pointed at a university in Malaysia (the URL is in the box at the top) ends up routing through Dublin, London, Washington, Newark, Palo Alto, Los Angeles, two cities in Malaysia, and finally on to Australia before it finds the university's server. (Like a bad plane flight!) This is another "shape" of the internet, which of course has no "shape" and is not, in that sense, visual.

The internet itself

The actual, physical, internet is a mass of hardware and cables. On the next two pages are photos of the router that runs UCC's email, and the cables leading out

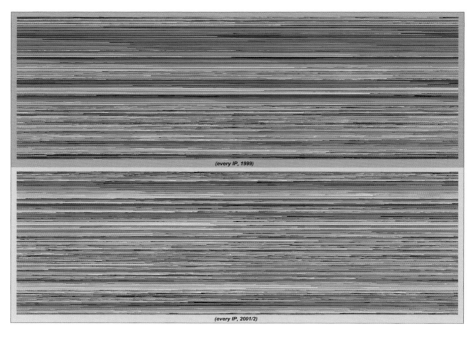

(every IP, 1999)

(every IP, 2001/2)

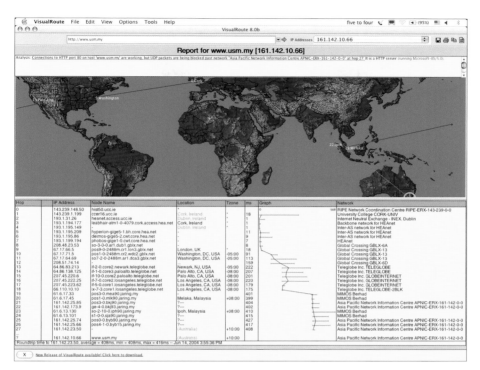

of the room — a typical tangle. (The exact location of the room is classified, and in fact the most difficult maps of the internet to obtain are actual physical plant maps. The internet exists, to some degree, as a series of classified locations.)

For further reading

http://www.nagios.org/; the Nagios system is documented and is freely available for download from this site. See also Rachel Greene, *Internet Art* (London: Thames and Hudson, 2004), 139-41 on Jevbratt; her site at jevbratt.com/1_to_1/; *Mappa mundi* at mappa.mundi.net/maps/; and *An Atlas of Cyberspaces* at www.cybergeography.org/atlas/topology.html.

9

Doing, Being and Becoming

Eithne Hunt

Occupation has been described in simple terms by Clare Hocking as "all of the ordinary and extraordinary things people do at home, at work and in their community that occupy their time." Ann Wilcock sees occupation as a synthesis of "doing, being, and becoming." She asserts that a dynamic balance between doing and being is central to healthful living and well-being. According to her, the development of a person or a community is dependent on both doing and being.

Health through occupation, and creative occupation in particular, has been integral to the beliefs and practice of the Occupational Therapy profession since its inception during the era of the Arts and Crafts movement. Canadian Occupational Therapist Judith Friedland, in her Muriel Driver Memorial Lecture in 2003, asked the question "Why crafts?." She traced the roots of Occupational Therapy to the soil of English and American political, social and artistic ideals prominent at the turn of the 20th century. The Arts and Crafts Movement, the Settlement House Movement (a social reform movement that originated in England in the early 1880s) and the Mental Hygiene Movement (an American movement, founded in the early 1900s to promote mental health and prevent mental illness) all recognized the importance of art for all, of community interdependence, of increased self-esteem, habit and skill development through the use of crafts.

The initial treatment tool of the Occupational Therapy profession was therapeutic occupation in the form of crafts, as Judith Friedland has described. Now, at the beginning of the twenty-first century, the profession is urged to reclaim its ethos with a reaffirmed commitment to the ideals and values of the founders. Creative occupations in particular, are the subject of renewed interest in occupational science and occupational therapy. With this "renaissance of occupation" (to borrow a phrase coined by Gail Whiteford, Elizabeth Townsend and Clare Hocking in 2000) comes a resurgence of interest in the transformative power of creative occupations, the relationship between creativity and health and a call for

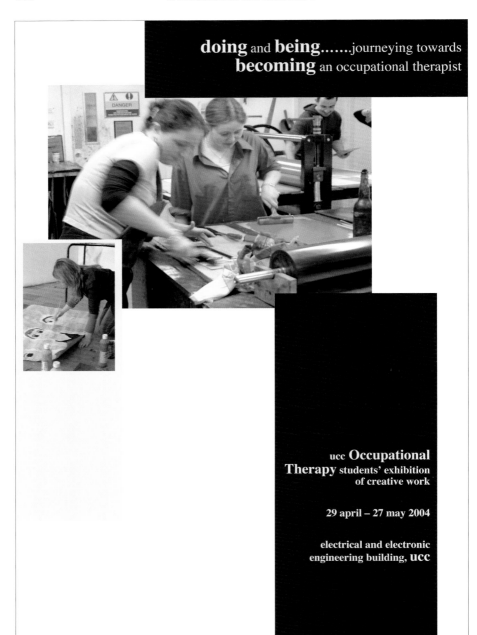

doing and **being**.......journeying towards **becoming** an occupational therapist

ucc **Occupational Therapy** students' exhibition of creative work

29 april – 27 may 2004

electrical and electronic engineering building, **ucc**

the custom design of powerful occupation-based therapeutic interventions to meet individual client or community need. These new directions have been well articulated by Victoria Holder, Doris Pierce, Suzanne Peloquin and Therese Schmid, among others.

Students' work

First year Occupational Therapy students at University College Cork have the opportunity to explore and experience firsthand the power and value of meaningful engagement in creative occupations. For six weeks in year one, they pursue their choice of art, photography, textiles or printmaking, in groups of eight students each. Each session lasts three hours. The experience culminates in a public exhibition of students' work. This exhibition is accompanied by a booklet, in which students write about their image and their experience of producing it. The class of 2003-2004 explored the theme of "doing, being and becoming."

Critique of this image practice

A potential weakness of this use of visual imagery is a tendency to place more value on the final product or chosen exhibited image. The real strength and core purpose of this image practice in terms of student learning is the experience of the process of making the image.

Students have reported experiencing fulfilment, belong, accomplishment, discovery, challenge, reward, growth in confidence and self-esteem, relaxation, enjoyment, fun, and pride in their work. This transformative "doing" and "being" experience is invaluable to students at the beginning stage of their journey towards "becoming" creative Occupational Therapists and designers of Occupational Therapy intervention for the 21st century.

Three examples of this work are included to illustrate the student's journey through the process of doing and being in these creative sessions-along with an image representing the end product: the final exhibition of work to which staff, students, family and friends are invited. However, we are not reproducing any of the images here, in order to underscore that what matters here is process.

Three students: Caitriona O'Connell, Louise Barrett and Sarah McCoy

Caitriona O' Connell, who produced a set of four photographs called *The Hands of Time*, writes:

> Occupational Therapists work with hands in many different ways, through splinting, hand exercises, art and craft work, involving people of all different ages. In my photographs, I have shown hands of different ages in various natural positions. I feel my

photographs fit the theme "Doing, Being and Becoming" as they show the hands doing activities, while being in natural positions and becoming older.

In the photo that opens this Chapter, Occupational Therapy student Louise Barrett is shown engaged in the process of "doing" her chosen creative occupation of printmaking. In the booklet that accompanied the exhibition, Louise wrote "with these six weeks [of printmaking], I found myself having a greater understanding of why creativity and groups are so important in occupational therapy. It is not so much the product of the sessions that were important. The process and the feelings that accompanied the process are what made me think about the therapeutic aspects of creativity… Also the feelings of fulfillment, belongingness and meaningful productivity made me aware of how much sessions such as these can benefit a client's interpersonal and intrapersonal well-being."

In the photo below, Occupational Therapy student Sarah McCoy reviews an image she produced in the printmaking session. Sarah wrote that "the print rep-

resents more than an end product. It is symbolic of the process of doing, an experience I found to be extremely enjoyable and therapeutic. I appreciated learning new skills. This gave me a great sense of accomplishment, which in turn
boosted my self–esteem."

Images for process and for use

It is interesting to speculate on the ways Occupational Therapy's interest in images differs from other uses in this book. With a few exceptions — including
Chapter 20 — very little in this book is oriented toward the *process* of making.
The scientific and technical images often require a great deal of attention to process, in the service of the single, finished image. Here, the exhibition that ended
the class required special attention, because it was important that the students
did not gear all their efforts to one final product, thus potentially undermining
the experience of the process. Perhaps different to the scientific and other non-art
images in this book, the images shown here work interactively, changing the
maker as well as that which is made.

For further reading

C. Archer, "Towards an Occupational Understanding of Apraxia," Master's thesis, University of South Australia, Adelaide, Australia, unpublished, 1998 ("It is through doing":
p. 11); Judith Friedland, "Why Crafts? Influences on the Development of Occupational
Therapy in Canada from 1890 to 1930," *Canadian Journal of Occupational Therapy* 70
no. 4 (2003): 204-12; Victoria Holder, "The Use of Creative Activities Within Occupational Therapy," *British Journal of Occupational Therapy*. 64 no. 2 (2001): 103-5; Doris
Pierce, *Occupation by Design: Building Therapeutic Power* (Philadelphia: F.A. Davis,
2003); Gail Whiteford, Elizabeth Townsend and Clare Hocking, "Reflections on a Renaissance of Occupation," *Canadian Journal of Occupational Therapy* 67 no. 1 (2000): 61-69;
and Ann Allart Wilcock, "Reflections on Doing, Being and Becoming" *Australian Occupational Therapy Journal* 46 (1999): 1-11; Hocking, "Creating Occupational Practice:
A Multidisciplinary Health Focus," in *Becoming an advanced healthcare practitioner*,
edited by G. Brown, S.A. Esdaile & S.E. Ryan (Edinburgh: Butterworth Heinemann,
2003), 189-215, quotation on p. 190; Peloquin, "Embracing our Ethos, Reclaiming our
Heart," *American Journal of Occupational Therapy* 59 no. 6 (2005): 611-625; Schmid,
Promoting Health Through Creativity, edited by T. Schmid (London: Whurr Publishers,
2005).

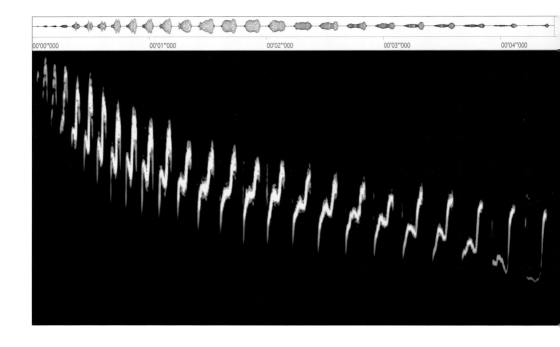

00'00"000   00'01"000   00'02"000   00'03"000   00'04"000

10

Visual Representation of Speech and Sounds

Paul Fletcher and James Elkins

Spectrograms reveal the acoustic nature of sound in two dimensions. The horizontal axis records time. The dark spectrogram is the song of the canyon wren; it is a series of rapid rising notes. As the song goes on — really only four seconds — the little rising notes fall, and to a human ear the result is a falling melody. The green spectrogram is part of the lark sparrow's song. It is much more complex, and over the course of three seconds it makes many rhythmic and tonal changes. To an unaided human ear, it sounds like lovely chirping, but with the help of the sonogram it is possible to hear much more — the visual dissection helps the ear to discern things that would otherwise be too rapid to catch.

Bird sonograms are increasingly popular, and several software packages make them accessible to amateurs. The Bird sonograms at the beginning and the end of this Chapter were made using software called Raven and Amadeus; the former is used by professional ornithologists.

Human speech spectrograms

In the spectrogram on the next page, someone is saying "the rain in Spain"; it takes less than 1 1/2 seconds.

The second dimension of a spectrogram, after time, is frequency, in this case measured from 0 to 8000 cycles per second (cps, or Hertz). Frequency is labelled on the y axis. The human ear can detect frequencies from 15 Hz to 20,000 Hz, and the voice includes frequencies higher than those shown here.

The third dimension is intensity (loudness). Here color represents loudness: black corresponds to the lowest volume, and louder sounds move through violet, blue, yellow, and orange, to red.

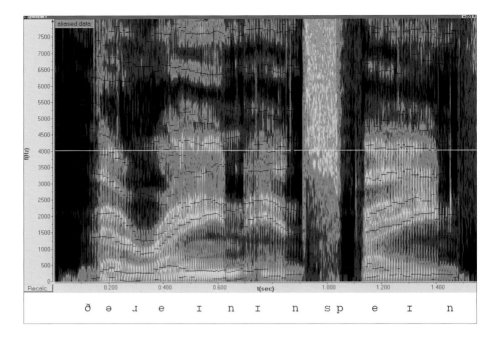

The continuous acoustic signal

The acoustic signal is continuous. Because the linguistic representation that we are most familiar with is the written form, we tend to think that words have spaces between them. As you can see, this is not the case. There is some black on the spectrogram, which signals silence, but the most obvious instance comes within a word, when the "p" sound in "Spain" is being pronounced. This is because in producing this sound you close your lips very briefly (for less than one-tenth of a second) and no sound comes out.

Vowels

You will see concentrations of acoustic energy, some colored red, in the lower half of the frequency range, between 500 and 2000 Hz. These are characteristic of vowels, and each of the vowels has three obvious arc-shaped concentrations, called 'formants'. It is the shape of these *formants*, their relationship to one another, and their duration, that enables us to identify different vowels.

    Formants are a little like harmonics in music, but not as predictable. They are resonance frequences overlaid on the fundamental frequency by the structure of the vocal tract. We hear the vowels in "rain" and "Spain" as the same. In the spectrogram, their formants have the same shape, are in the same spatial orientation to one another, and are the same length. The individual sounds are identified below the spectrogram using symbols from the International Phonetic Alphabet (IPA). This is used because English orthography can be misleading, especially as to the sounds of vowels.

Accents

The quality of vowels is very important in distinguishing accents of English. Here are two spectrograms comparing the word "caught" spoken by a native of Tralee in Ireland, and by a native of Bandon, both female and of similar ages. Once again IPA symbols under the spectrogram identifies the different sounds in the words. (This is a funny comparison to people in Ireland: Tralee is a tourist destination, and home of a popular beauty contest; Bandon, to put it politely, isn't a tourist destination.)

Most noticeable is the difference in the length of the vowels. The Bandon vowel is shorter and sounds more like the vowel in "cot," while the Tralee pronunciation is longer. The shape of the formants differs also. Most relevant to our identification of accentual differences are the first three formants. Formants higher up the range (easier to see in the Tralee vowel) are important in identifying individual differences between speakers.

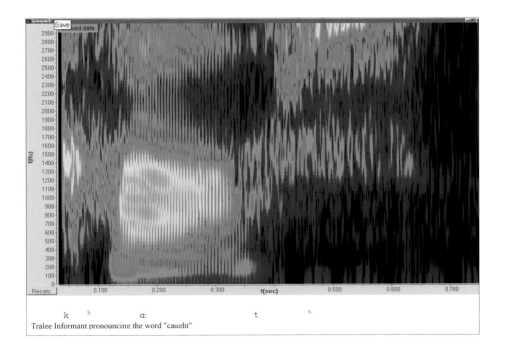

Tralee Informant pronouncing the word "caught"

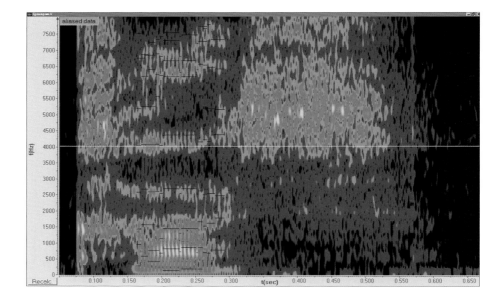

Individual speakers

Phonograms are common in the mass media when they are shown as "voice-prints": ways of identifying individual speakers on audiotapes. Such differences are very subtle. The Bandon speaker's voice looks "rougher": the corrugations are glottal (laryngeal) pulses, possibly traits of that individual speaker.

Phoneticians distinguish between speaker verification and elimination (which is relatively easy) and speaker identification (which is prone to error). In the first cases one compares a spectrogram from speaker A with a previously stored spectrogram from speaker A, or another speaker. Speaker identification (the voiceprint case) is much trickier, and informed research would suggest that it cannot yet be done reliably.

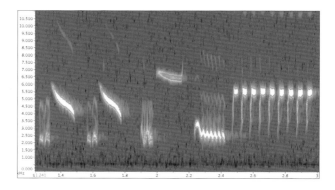

Spectrograms as pictures

Spectrograms are a good example of one of the themes proposed in the Introduction: they look like naturalistic images, but they aren't. (There have already been several examples, in Chapters 1 and 6.) Somehow, their image-like configuration makes them more useful than they might be if their information were presented in tabular form (as in the Nagios software discussed in Chapter 7). Somehow, they help us to discern what we hear more accurately. Birdwatchers slow down spectrograms so they can pry apart the rapid changes in birdsong, and there are ways of exaggerating the vertical scale and the color schema. But even without those enhancements, the picturelike quality of the spectrograms lets them speak — or sing — more clearly.

For further reading

A. Hughes and P. Trudgill, *English Accents and Dialects* (London: Arnold, 1996); R. Kent and C. Read, *Acoustic Analysis of Speech,* second edition (Albany NY: Singular, 2002); P. Ladefoged, *Vowels and Consonants* (Oxford: Blackwell Publishers, 2001); David Rothenberg, *Why Birds Sing: A Journey Through the Mystery of Bird Song* (New York: Basic Books, 2005).

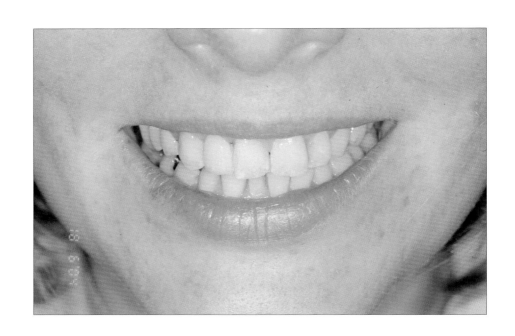

11

Matching Shades of Crowns
Francis Burke and Catherine Gorman

It may seem that teeth just range from sparkly white to tea-stain brown: that would be a simple change in hue, and a lowering of value. But in fact some teeth have a wide color range, and they also vary in chroma. (Color is best quantified according to its three dimensions: hue, for example blue, red, or green; the chroma, which is the intensity or saturation of color; and the value, the level of brightness of the color.)

The challenge for dentists is that the differences in the hue, value, and chroma of individual teeth are very subtle but crucial to providing the patient with a crown that matches perfectly. (Artists have it easy by comparison!)

Vita's first method

Vita Zahnfabrik in Bad Sackingen, Germany, is a large dental company. They offer two arrangements.

In the first (top photo on the next page), porcelain teeth are grouped into four categories: A, B, C, and D. Notice the small letters at the base of the teeth.) Each represents a different hue. Each category is subdivided into numbers: A1, A2, A3, A3.5, A4. Here the number represents the chroma (intensity). The teeth can be arranged from lightest to darkest for comparison of value to the natural teeth.

Vita's second method

In the 3-D Master Toothguide, the shade samples are grouped in 5 lightness levels (values). (See the bottom photo on the next page.) This arrangement incorporates all three dimensions of color perception; the manufacturers claim this results in increased accuracy when selecting a shade. Value is selected first; in this example the dentist selects the three teeth labelled 3M.

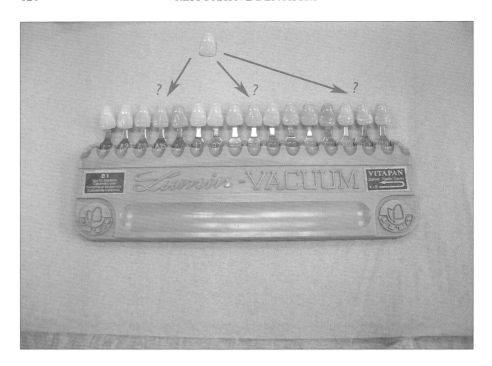

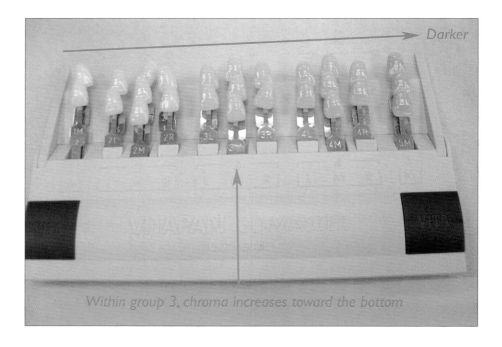

The three teeth here are labelled 3M1, 3M2, and 3M3. The differences between them are higher and lower chroma (intensity). And finally, the hue is decided (L,M,R).

Color wheels

Notice how subtle this is, in comparison to ordinary color wheels. Can you see, for example, that the three teeth in the vertical row 3M differ in chroma (intensity) and *not* in value (darkness)? That the teeth in the third grouping differ in hue? The ones on the right are more red, and the ones on the left are more yellow.

This level of subtlety is beyond most instruction in art academies, where Josef Albers's *Interaction of Color* is generally considered the most detailed source. (The colors in his book are more obvious than these.)

Color sensitivity

In the original exhibition on which this book is based, we offered a model of teeth , a mirror, and a color-corrected lamp. Visitors were encouraged to compare the porcelain samples with their teeth, and see if they could name the color classifications of each of their teeth.

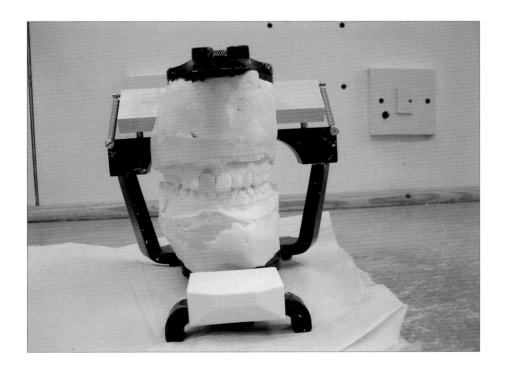

The makers of porcelain teeth recommend that dentists only compare tooth colors for five to seven seconds at a stretch, because the colors are so close in value, hue, and chroma that the eye's sensitivity begins to trail off. Very little in the art world compares with this degree of sensitivity: the closest parallel would be professional printers, who have to be very accurate in matching print runs and in approximating the colors of original prints when they are reproduced; but there is software and hardware for those tasks. In art education, Joseph Albers's *Interaction of Color* (1963) remains a standard textbook. It is used in conjunction with colored papers, and one of Albers's purposes was to increase artists' sensitivity to minute changes in hue and chroma. But even that text — in its many abridged editions and computer implementations — does not come anywhere near the precision required in matching porcelain teeth. In terms of visual subtlety and sheer discriminatory accuracy, the techniques described in this section surpass even art and history of art.

For further reading

Shimya Hobo et al., editors, *Fundamentals of Fixed Prosthodontics*, third edition (Chicago IL: Quintessence, 1997); N. Ray, "Color and Color Matching" (unpublished manuscript, 1998, University College Cork, available at www.ucc.ie/ucc/depts/restorative/downloads.htm); and R.W. Dykema, C.J. Goodacre, and R.W. *Phillips Johnston's Modern Practice in Fixed Prosthodontics,* fourth edition (Philadelphia PA: W.B. Saunders, 2001); Elkins, *How to Use Your Eyes* (New York: Routledge, 2000), chapter 27, "How to Look at Color."

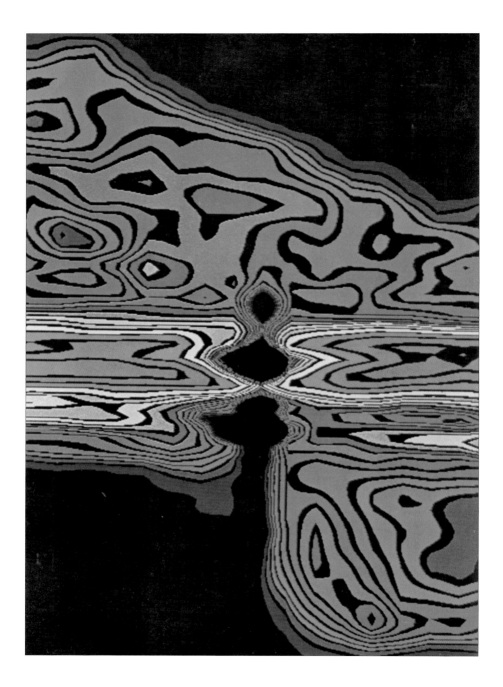

12

Mapping Clouds at the Galactic Center

Gerard Wrixon, Paul Callanan, James Elkins

This image appears at first to be a naturalistic picture of something: but it is in fact a diagram. The horizontal axis is spatial — a sweep of the area just left and right of the center of the galaxy. The vertical axis, however, is coded — it records the speed at which clouds of Hydrogen are moving toward or away from the galactic center.

The image does not show visible light, but rather records the intensities of radio wave emission at the specific wavelength of 21 centimeters — so it is a non-naturalistic image that records something that is, in any case, invisible to human eyes. (This is even aside from the fact that it shows a very tiny, faint area in the constellation Sagittarius, which is almost beyond the capacity of unaided vision.)

Reading the graph

The image originally appeared in *Scientific American* in 1974, accompanied by the graphical key reproduced on the next page. To interpret the image, imagine the strip that is apparently left and right of the Galactic center: within it, gases are moving at different speeds, and at different distances from us. The red area on the image has little or no velocity: it represents the Hydrogen in our line of sight, left and right of the Galactic center. Negative values on the y axis mean gases moving toward us, and vice versa. The bit of orange and yellow at the right margin, below the red center line, named the "3-kiloparsec arm," is a cloud of Hydrogen moving toward us at about 50 kilometers per second. The green area above, labelled "arm expanding at 135 kilometers per second," is moving away from us.

The lower right of the image is very fast-moving Hydrogen — up to 200 kilometers per second — moving toward us, and the upper left is Hydrogen moving away. In both cases, the high velocities mean the gases are near the Galactic center.

The Center of the Galaxy   14

by R. H. Sanders and G. T. Wrixon
April 1974

*Coded in the radio, infrared and X-ray emissions from
the invisible nucleus of our galaxy is mounting
evidence that it is periodically the scene of titanic
explosions*

Our galaxy is a disk-shaped collection of stars, gas and dust whose components are all bound together by their mutual gravitational attraction. Like an enormous pinwheel it rotates majestically around its mysterious nucleus, or central region. From our vantage near the edge of the disk the nucleus has until quite recently been hidden by clouds of obscuring dust. Within the past 20 years, however, new techniques of "looking" through the dust have been developed, providing us with tantalizing glimpses of the nuclear region. Piecing together observations made through "windows" at wavelengths both longer and shorter than those of visible light, astronomers have become aware of striking similarities between our galactic center and the nuclei of certain bizarre objects called Seyfert galaxies.

Seyfert galaxies are named for Carl K. Seyfert, who in 1943 first classified a group of galaxies according to the unusual properties of their nucleus. They are spiral galaxies (disk-shaped galaxies with luminous spiral arms like our own galaxy) characterized by a small, very bright nucleus embedded in rapidly moving masses of gas that are apparently being ejected from the central region. Seyfert nuclei are also a rich source of infrared radiation and radio waves. Indeed, Seyfert nuclei emit such large amounts of energy and matter that our present laws of physics may be inadequate to explain them.

Quasars, which were discovered in the early 1960's, may be even more extreme examples of the phenomenon seen in Seyfert galaxies. Quasars are very

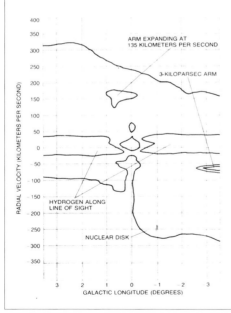

GAS MOTIONS AT GALACTIC CENTER are displayed in the computer-generated contour map on the opposite page. Based on observations made with the 140-foot radio telescope of the National Radio Astronomy Observatory at Green Bank, W.Va., the map shows the distribution of emission from un-ionized hydrogen at a wavelength of 21 centimeters. The different colors indicate the intensity of the 21-centimeter line, ranging from violet (lowest level) to red (highest level). The vertical axis, as shown at the left, does not indicate galactic latitude but rather the velocity of hydrogen lying in the galactic plane: velocities toward us are negative, velocities away from us are positive. The horizontal red ridge centered at zero velocity represents all the un-ionized hydrogen along the line of sight on either side of the galactic center. The deep hole at the center identifies where 21-centimeter radiation from the powerful radio source known as Sagittarius A is absorbed by un-ionized hydrogen lying between it and us. To the right and just below the central ridge, at a negative velocity of more than 50 kilometers per second, is a fainter ridge produced by emission from the "three-kiloparsec arm." Since the three-kiloparsec arm also produces an absorption line in the output of Sagittarius A, the arm is on this side of the center, and since its velocity is negative it is expanding away from the center and toward us. At the lower right there is a ridge of emission (*blue-and-green feature*) whose maximum velocity exceeds 200 kilometers per second. This ridge is emission from the nuclear disk; its high velocity means that it is very near the galactic center and rotating rapidly. Notice that the velocity approaches zero toward the galactic center. Above and to the left of the center the picture is somewhat ambiguous. The dominant feature is a ridge of emission (*green band*) that crosses the position of the galactic center at $+135$ kilometers per second; hence it is an expanding arm of gas moving away from us. The absence of an absorption hole at the position of Sagittarius A means that the expanding arm is on the other side of the nucleus. The program for generating the color contour map was devised by Thomas Cram and David Ehnebuske.

In three dimensions

Because we are more or less in the Galactic plane, we see the center edge-on. The image therefore encodes a picture of gases rotating around the center, like the spiral arms of stars in the Galaxy as a whole.

Very high-velocity Hydrogen is rotating close in to the center. Lower-velocity Hydrogen is farther away: one arm swings around toward us, on the right; and a second swings away from us on the left. It is not easy to visualize this, but it is a typical exercise in scientific illustration.

The limits of the image

There are, perhaps, two limitations to this image. First, it has relatively few data points. The isobars are really line segments (made jagged by the large pixels) that connect one data point to the next. That is an insuperable limitation because 21-centimeter radio emissions cannot be made more detailed.

Another limitation comes from the *use* the image was meant to have. In 1974 the idea of black holes was new. To test whether or not a black hole might be present, Sanders and Wrixon made a "model galaxy" simulation on a "large electronic computer" and "observed" it as they observed the actual Galaxy. By changing the mass of the central object, and seeing how the model matched their image, they concluded that whatever lies at the Galactic center could be as large as 200 million solar masses — within the range of a black hole. Thus the image was augmented by a computer model, and would have been incomplete without it.

2004

The first of these limitations — resolution — is easily improved by searching for emissions other than 21 centimeter Hydrogen emissions. Carbon monoxide, for example, has several characteristic emission wavelengths, among them 0.065 centimeters (461 GHz), which are caused by a particular quantum jump in the atoms, from $J = 4 \rightarrow 3$.

In 2004, thirty years after Sanders's and Wrixon's study, a team led by Christopher Martin produced the images reproduced below. Each frame is a longitude-velocity graph like Sanders's and Wrixon's; the middle one samples the Galactic center, and the others show the level (galactic latitude) just above and below it.

The left-right range in degrees is about the same as Sanders's and Wrixon's diagram, but the smaller wavelength allows much higher resolution. Because these images sample carbon dioxide clouds and not hydrogen, they are hard to compare with the 1974 diagram — and they hint at the complexity of the region.

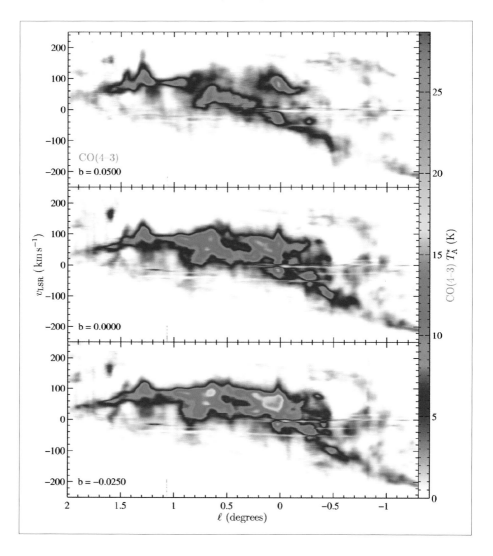

Face-on views

Another recent development is the computer-aided calculation of face-on views, showing the Galactic center "from above." One is shown here.

The center is now known to be comprised of at least three sources, known as Sgr A*, B, and C, and they orbit the Galactic center. This image records gas thermal pressure in another emission line of carbon monoxide. The authors of the study posit a model with four bodies (Sgr A*, B, C, and an object known as the "1.3° region") rotating around one another in two or more spiral arms.

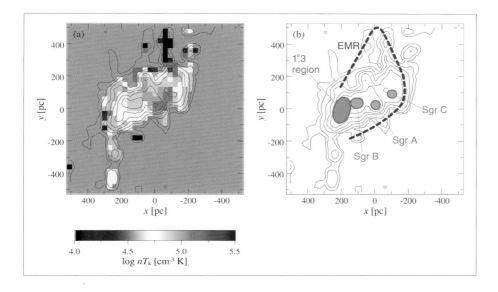

Clouds, shells, arcs...

Martin notes that the region close to the Galactic center has "a complex distribution of emission, which is chaotic, asymmetric, and non-planar, [with] hundreds of clouds, shells, arcs, rings, and filaments." (A little farther from the center, at the distances studied by Sanders and Wrixon, the new study confirms "the gas is loosely organized around closed orbits.") There

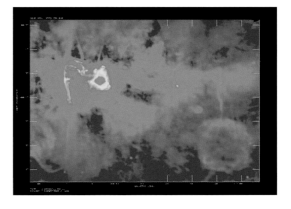

are even star clusters near the center, named "the Arches" and "the Quintuplet." The picture is gradually becoming more complex, if not clearer.

This photo is another radio-frequency image, at 1.4 GHz. F. Yusef-Zadeh, who published this image on January 15, 2005, compares the Galactic center to "a jungle where many species evolve, share the same resources and interact with each other."

Optimal resolution

Recently, too, there has been interest in "non-thermal filaments" (NTFs), long, thin clouds that are only found near the Galactic center. Astronomers have managed to map them in detail even though they are less than an arcminute in apparent length — that is less than one-sixtieth the width of one of the grid squares in the *Scientific American* graph. (For comparison: one arcminute is one-thirtieth the diameter of the full Moon — a tiny portion of the sky.) Yet there is no way to achieve perfect resolution of nebulous objects, because the objects themselves have arbitrarily defined boundaries.

Point-like objects are another matter, and studies of stars at the Galactic center are well advanced. Infrared studies of stars have achieved amazing resolutions. Photo above is about 20 arcminutes wide, about the size of the central black area in the first image.

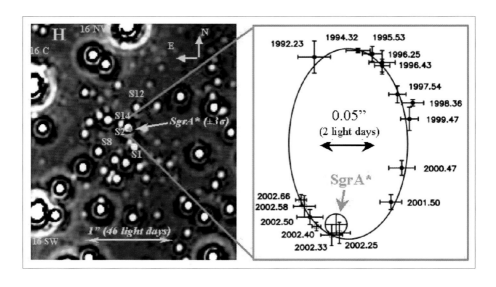

The bottom photo on the last page, in turn, is a detail of that tiny portion, zooming in on the enigmatic Sagittarius A (marked Sgr A*). The arrow shows the scale: one arcsecond, which is one-sixtieth of the width of one of the squares in the 1974 image. At that resolution it is possible to plot individual stars as they orbit around Sgr A*. (As this book goes to press, scientists at the Max-Planck-Institut für extraterrestrische Physik have released a movie of the motion of the stars in this region, pushing the limits of resolution still further).

What comprises a perfect image?

The conundrum here is the resolution of irresolvable objects. The same problem is of concern in images of the earliest pre-galactic objects at the edge of the visible universe, which will be targets of the Next Generation Space Telescope: they overlap and have no distinct boundaries. What is required is a mathematical constraint on what counts as an "object": a situation far from the concerns of image making in daily life or in art.

Of these images, the one that is most strongly counter-intuitive is the first, because it only appears to be a picture like some later ones. It is, rather, a graph posing as a naturalistic picture — asking to be read, illegitimately, as a picture — a theme that recurs in several of these chapters.

For further reading

Chrisopher Martin et al., "The AST/RO Survey of the Galactic Center Region. I. The Inner 3 Degrees," *ApJS* 150 (2004): 239, plate 6; Tsuyoshi Sawada et al., "A Molecular Face-on View of the Galactic Centre Region," arXiv:astro-ph/0401286 v1 15 Jan 2004, Fig. 11; F. Yusef-Zadeh et al., "Starburst Driven Thermal and Non-thermal Structures in the Galactic Center Region," Fig. 1; T. Ott et al., "Inward Bound: Studying The Galactic Center With Naos/Conica," figs. 1 and 4. See also T. Viehmann et al., "*L*- and *M*-band Imaging Observations of the Galactic Center Region," arXiv:astro-ph/0411798 v1 30 Nov 2004, and Johannes Staguhn et al., "350 μm Galactic Center Dust Observations with SHARC II," arXiv:astro-ph/0412148 v1 6 Dec 2004. For the movie of the stars and the galactic center, see www.mpe.mpg.de/ir/GC/prop.html.

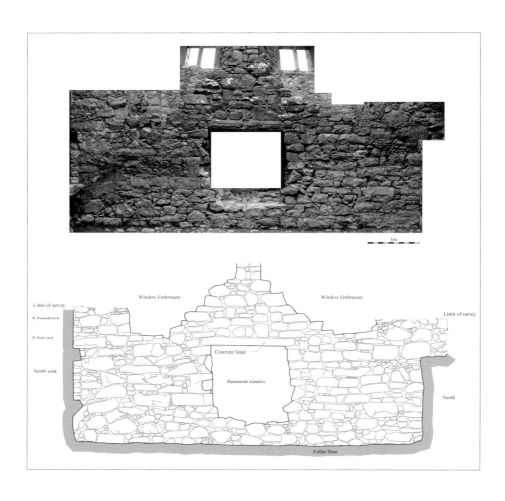

1m

13

The Repertoire of Archaeological Images

Hugh Kavanagh

Archaeology, it could be argued, is one of the most visually-oriented and visually intensive disciplines in the university. Much archaeological research is carried out by inspecting maps and plans of previously recorded monuments. Newly discovered sites are meticulously mapped and recorded using a variety of media and methods.

The visual methods of archaeology range from wholly automated images (for example, aerial photographs) to freehand drawings. Here is a sample.

Cumulative mapping

Archaeologists record the exact position of sites using Global Positioning data. Large compendia of archaeological sites will often give these data, called GIS, for Geographic Information Systems. (Global Positioning data has been abused in the United States by people who use them to find and loot remote sites.)

The image on the next two pages was made by overlaying GIS information from the Heritage Service onto an Ordinance Survey vector map, at a scale of 1:50,000. It shows every archaeological site in County Cork, Ireland. That kind of manipulation can be done using automated software — in this case, AutoCAD Map 2004.

Older images

At the other end of the time scale, archaeologists make use of historical images. The image on nineteenth-century copy of an earlier painting looking down along what today is Castle Street, Cork. The painting shows a ship entering the city between the King's and Queens castle: a motif that was repeated in the Cork city coast of arms.

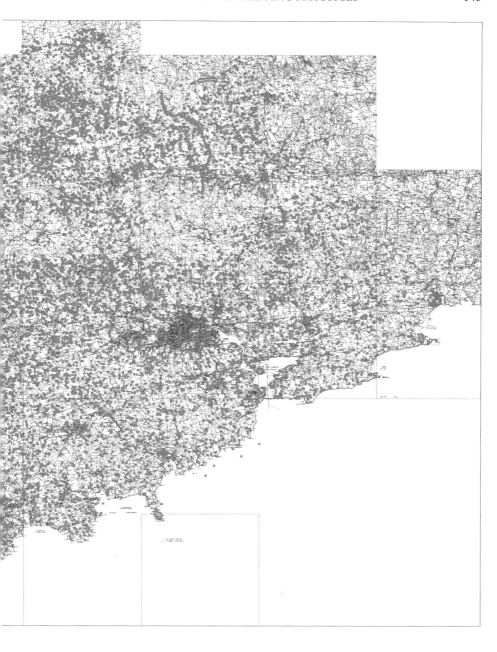

Development planning

Archaeologists are commonly involved in issues of planning.
This AutoCAD drawing on the next page combines four sources:
1. Geo-referenced aerial mapping (upper left)
2. Second- and third-edition Ordinance Survey mapping (lower left, right)
3. Technical development drawings from the client (red line)
4. GIS information from the Department of the Environment, Heritage and local government (circled).

Combining this graphical information aids the archaeologist in advising developers where archaeological impacts can be avoided or minimized. In this case, the subject is a proposed gas pipeline.

Urban sites

The image on page 146 depicts excavations are being carried on at 35-39 Main Street, Cork, behind the city library.

This drawing shows the excavation in relation to an Ordinance Survey map at a scale of 1:1,000. Note the detail: every street address is given. *Mh* stands for "manhole"; *LS* for "light standard."

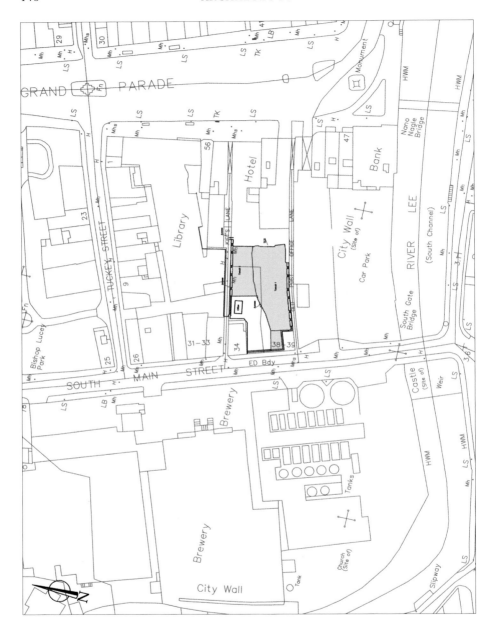

Survey drawings

At times archaeologists use skills associated with architects and engineers, as in this study of the Cork Waterworks. The Adobe Illustrator drawing on page 147 shows two examples of building survey techniques. The chimney elevation is carried out using traditional surveying methods and also using a surveyor's "EDM total station" (*EDM,* for "electromagnetic distance measuring": lasers calculate distances automatically).

The steam engine elevation was created by extrapolating details from a 3D "point cloud" measured by a laser scanner. (For more on laser scanners, see Chapter 22.)

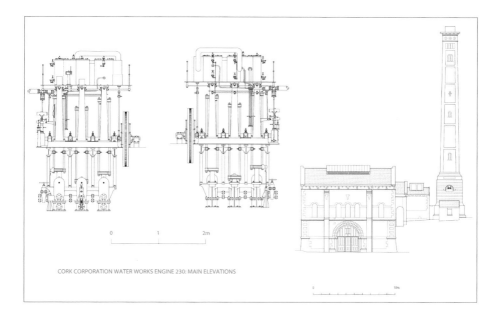

CORK CORPORATION WATER WORKS ENGINE 230: MAIN ELEVATIONS

Photogrammetric surveys

Another way to create an elevation is by "rubbersheeting" many separate digital photographs to make an accurate, undistorted photographic elevation.

The image reproduced at the beginning of this Chapter shows a wall at Burncourt Castle, Co. Tipperary. Fixed points were surveyed using a "total station"; those points then corrected the mosaic of digital photos. Notice that the wall with windows is distorted: it is beyond the picture plane of the corrected wall.

Technical plans

The image on the next page is a technical is a technical *in situ* plan, originally drawn in pencil on drafting film (a kind of paper made from duralar polyester that is used in technical drawing), using grid lines and coordinates. The pencil

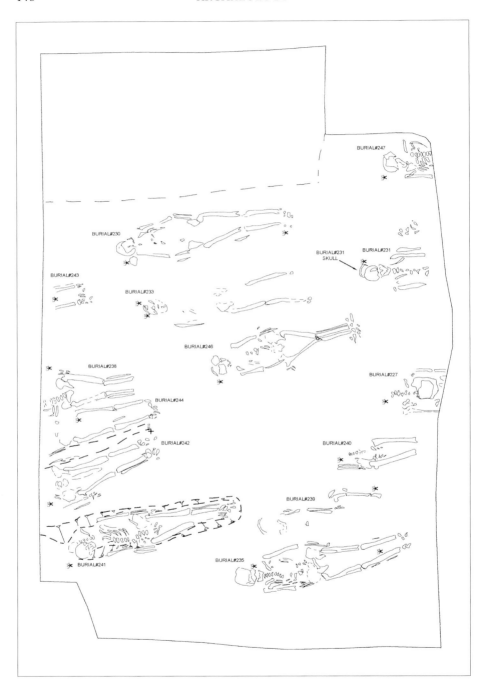

drawings were then converted into digital formats, as shown. (In the past, the pencil would have been gone over with permanent ink.)

Measured drawings

Another kind of drawing that is hand-done is the cross-section and elevation of individual objects, like these Bronze Age pots found at Castlehyde, Fermoy.

The details displayed here may only be obvious to a trained archaeologist, any superfluous details that might seem important to a casual observer are omitted. In other words, they are not simply realistic but selective in what they record.

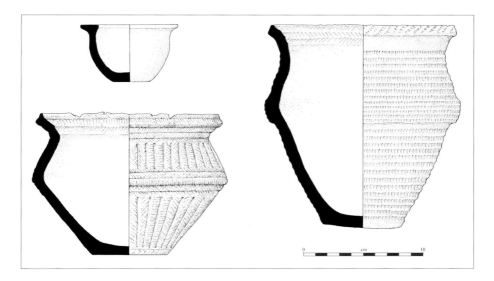

Computers versus hand drawing

Freehand drawing has a marginal, but essential place in several disciplines. In archaeology it can complement computer-assisted mapping.

The two pictures on the next page show a Bronze Age house at Curraghatoor, Co. Tipperary. The computer-assisted design has a speculative elevation (all that is known for sure is the positions of the bases of the stakes and posts). A freehand reconstruction restores a sense of scale and eliminates the intrusive detail typical of CAD (computer-assisted design).

Compatibility and the "thicket of images"

Some kinds of imaging work perfectly together; others are stand-alone. In that respect archaeology resembles the study of viruses, where no one kind of image

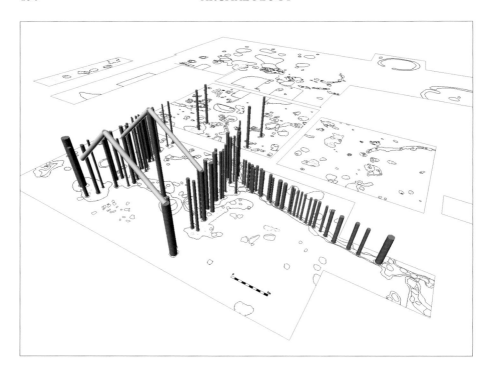

will do (that theme is also exemplified in Chapter 27, and elaborated in the Introduction). There are interesting parallels between disciplines that require multiple kinds of pictures: they each involve objects that have more than one level of detail (like fractal objects, they change depending on how closely they are observed); and they involve technologies that only work at certain scales (move in too close to a virus, and you need a different kind of microscopic technique; move in too close to an archaeological site, and you need a new map). It would be interesting to develop a general theory of such incompatibilities: a possible project for a future image science.

Emotional power

But all these techniques come down to the subject matter of archaeology: people's lives. The excavation of skeletons in particular is an emotional subject, but it must be carried out in the most accurate and objective manner possible. That is one of the paradoxes of archaeology: its battery of scientific illustrations can be used to capture the most personal and moving subjects.

Some of the finds result in images of extraordinary power, strangely at odds with the desiccated, scientific images that preceded them. In this case the subject is a burial site in which a woman's child is interred between her legs.

For further reading:

Ken Dark, *Theoretical Archaeology* (Ithaca NY: Cornell University Press, 1995); *The Student's Guide to Archaeological Illustrating,* edited by Brian Dillon (Los Angeles: University of California Press, 1985); Lesley and Roy Adkins, *Archaeological Illustration* (Cambridge NY: Cambridge University Press, 1989); and www.gisuser.com.au/MM/content/2001/MM16/feature/MM16_feature.html.

14

A Geological Map

Ivor A. J. MacCarthy

Geologists' maps are concentrated repositories of information, like non-visual databases in some other disciplines. Nominally, they present the distribution of various geological formations on the Earth's surface; they are based on examination of rock outcrops, but also on subsurface information such as boreholes and geophysical surveys.

In addition, they have a theoretical aspect; it lies partly in the fact that the geological composition of areas lying between data points must be interpreted. Maps also contain theoretical models of the structural composition and past environments in a region, and they model factors which may have affected sedimentation patterns during the infilling of ancient sedimentary basins.

Geological map of the South Munster Basin

This map describes and interprets the geology of the western part of the South Munster Basin in Ireland. This area was part of a large sedimentary basin measuring about 150km by 90km, which developed as an area of subsidence towards the end of the Devonian Period about 360 million years ago, much like the Lake Eyre Basin of Australia or the Tarim Basin of Tibet. Subsidence continued here until the middle of the Carboniferous Period, about 315 million years ago. The basin accumulated about 5km of sediment during that time in response to the varying environmental conditions, which were strongly influenced by climatic factors and fluctuations in global sea level. Subsequently, at the end of the Carboniferous Period (about 290 million years ago), the sediments infilling the basin were deformed by titanic plate tectonic forces which resulted in their deformation. This took the form of intense folding and fracturing. The deformed fill of that sedimentary basin now constitutes the bedrock of southern Munster.

The main map shows the distribution of the various rock types comprising the bedrock. The colors represent distinctive rock types or formations. Each formation is given a code which assists its identification in the Stratigraphy legend.

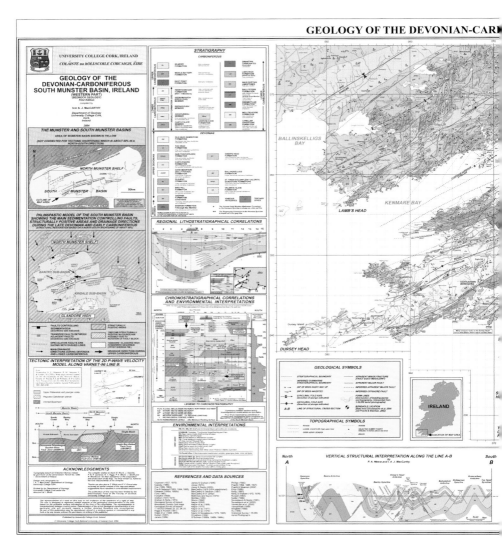

The map also shows a number of structural features such as faults and fractures in the bedrock. Also shown are the axes of folds such as anticlines (N-shaped folds) and synclines (*-shaped folds). The dip or inclination of the sedimentary layers is also shown. The thin black lines show the intersection of the layers with the surface, and are known as form lines.

SOUTH MUNSTER BASIN, IRELAND

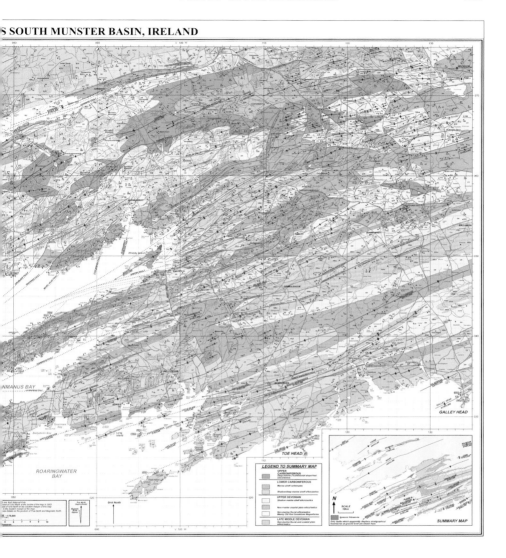

Inset drawings and maps

The boxes on the left-hand side and along the lower margin of the map provide further information on the geology of the area.

Stratigraphy

The various colored parts on the map show the areas underlain by particular rock types or formations. The legend shown on the next page identifies and describes these

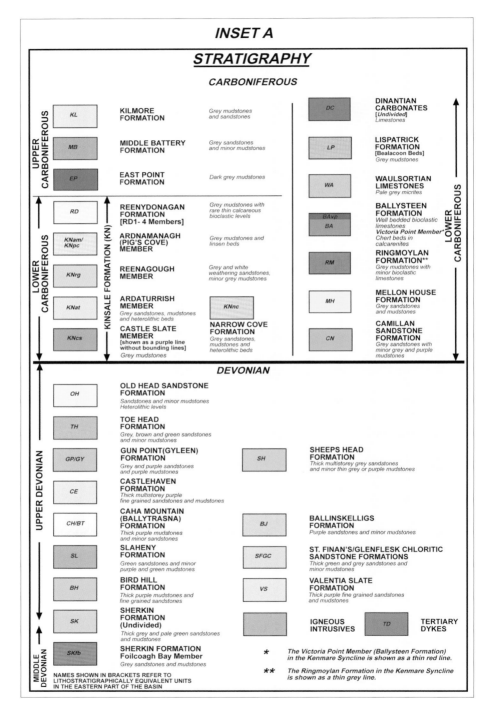

INSET A

STRATIGRAPHY

CARBONIFEROUS

UPPER CARBONIFEROUS

KL	KILMORE FORMATION	Grey mudstones and sandstones
MB	MIDDLE BATTERY FORMATION	Grey sandstones and minor mudstones
EP	EAST POINT FORMATION	Dark grey mudstones

LOWER CARBONIFEROUS — **KINSALE FORMATION (KN)**

RD	REENYDONAGAN FORMATION [RD1- 4 Members]	Grey mudstones with rare thin calcareous bioclastic levels
KNam/KNpc	ARDNAMANAGH (PIG'S COVE) MEMBER	Grey mudstones and linsen beds
KNrg	REENAGOUGH MEMBER	Grey and white weathering sandstones, minor grey mudstones
KNat	ARDATURRISH MEMBER	Grey sandstones, mudstones and heterolithic beds
KNcs	CASTLE SLATE MEMBER [shown as a purple line without bounding lines] Grey mudstones	
KNnc	NARROW COVE FORMATION	Grey sandstones, mudstones and heterolithic beds

LOWER CARBONIFEROUS

DC	DINANTIAN CARBONATES [Undivided] Limestones
LP	LISPATRICK FORMATION [Bealacoon Beds] Grey mudstones
WA	WAULSORTIAN LIMESTONES Pale grey micrites
BAvp / BA	BALLYSTEEN FORMATION Well bedded bioclastic limestones *Victoria Point Member* Chert beds in calcarenites
RM	RINGMOYLAN FORMATION** Grey mudstones with minor bioclastic limestones
MH	MELLON HOUSE FORMATION Grey sandstones and mudstones
CN	CAMILLAN SANDSTONE FORMATION Grey sandstones with minor grey and purple mudstones

DEVONIAN

UPPER DEVONIAN

OH	OLD HEAD SANDSTONE FORMATION Sandstones and minor mudstones Heterolithic levels
TH	TOE HEAD FORMATION Grey, brown and green sandstones and minor mudstones
GP/GY	GUN POINT(GYLEEN) FORMATION Grey and purple sandstones and purple mudstones
CE	CASTLEHAVEN FORMATION Thick multistory purple fine grained sandstones and mudstones
CH/BT	CAHA MOUNTAIN (BALLYTRASNA) FORMATION Thick purple mudstones and minor sandstones
SL	SLAHENY FORMATION Green sandstones and minor purple and green mudstones
BH	BIRD HILL FORMATION Thick purple mudstones and fine grained sandstones
SK	SHERKIN FORMATION (Undivided) Thick grey and pale green sandstones and mudstones

MIDDLE DEVONIAN

| SKfb | SHERKIN FORMATION Foilcoagh Bay Member Grey sandstones and mudstones |

SH	SHEEPS HEAD FORMATION Thick multistorey grey sandstones and minor thin grey or purple mudstones
BJ	BALLINSKELLIGS FORMATION Purple sandstones and minor mudstones
SFGC	ST. FINAN'S/GLENFLESK CHLORITIC SANDSTONE FORMATIONS Thick green and grey sandstones and minor mudstones
VS	VALENTIA SLATE FORMATION Thick purple fine grained sandstones and mudstones

| | IGNEOUS INTRUSIVES |
| TD | TERTIARY DYKES |

NAMES SHOWN IN BRACKETS REFER TO LITHOSTRATIGRAPHICALLY EQUIVALENT UNITS IN THE EASTERN PART OF THE BASIN

*   The Victoria Point Member (Ballysteen Formation) in the Kenmare Syncline is shown as a thin red line.

** The Ringmoylan Formation in the Kenmare Syncline is shown as a thin grey line.

formations and lists the order in which they were laid down. The oldest layers are at the base of the legend. The rock layers become younger as one ascends this legend. Each formation is given a two-letter code, which also appears on the map for ease of identification. The legend also gives a brief description of each formation in terms of its rock type. Also shown here are the geological ages of the rock formations.

Regional lithostratigraphical correlations

Just under the stratigraphy key is a drawing that shows what the rock layers would have looked like if a vertical section had been made across the basin after the rocks were deposited but before they were deformed at the end of the Carboniferous Period. The drawing shows how the thickness of the layers changes across the basin in a rough north-south direction. A scale bar is shown on the

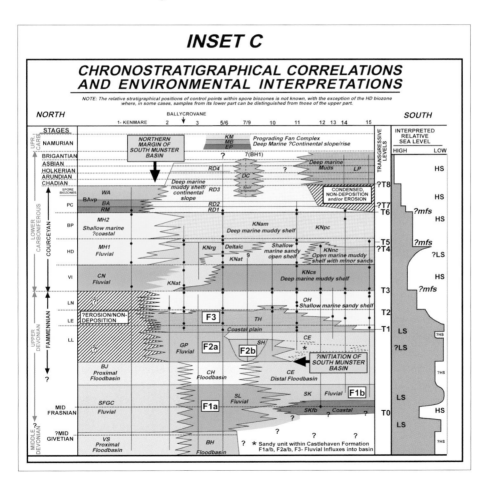

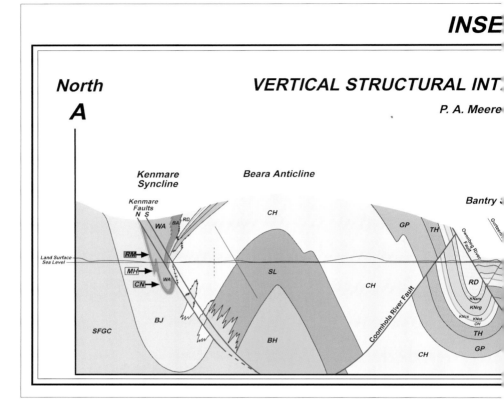

diagram for the vertical thickness (the scale is exaggerated for clarity). The smaller inset map shows the line of section and the data points.

Chronostratigraphical correlations and environmental interpretations

The legend reproduced on the previous page lists the full range of rock layers or formations according to their age, the formations becoming younger as one ascends the diagram. It also shows how the various formations change laterally across the basin. The vertical axis on this diagram represents geological time rather than thickness. The horizontal axis is distance. The various geological time intervals, known as "Stages", are listed on the left hand side of the diagram. These are determined by examination of fossils, in particular microfossils. These are shown as "Palynological control points." Palynology is the study of fossil plant spores and can be used to determine the relative age of sediments and their environment of deposition.

The diagram also presents interpretations of the environmental conditions which are thought to have been responsible for the deposition of the various rock forma-

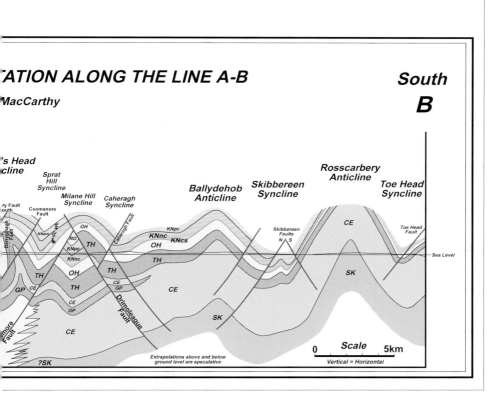

tions. Importantly, the diagram presents an interpretation of the relative sea level (rising or falling) during the course of the basin's history. This is the brown-colored graph on the right of the diagram. HS indicates relative high stands of sea level and LS represents relative low stand of sea level. T1 to T8 represent a number of "marine transgressions" or inundations into the area. "Maximum flooding surfaces" mark the farthest landward advance of the sea during a marine transgression. The diagram also shows the times when there were major influxes of sediment (F1, F2, F3) into the basin from the land located to the north and west at this time.

Vertical structural interpretation along the line A-B

This drawing allows one to understand the folding of the rock layers. It represents a side view of an imaginary vertical slice through the landscape. The slice goes from point *A* to *B* on the main map. The land surface is shown as a wavy line. It runs just above and below the straight horizonal line indicating sea level. The colors on the cross section correspond to the colors on the main map. If the wavy horizontal line is followed the same succession of colors are encountered as one follows the line from A to B on the main map. This diagram also extrapolates upwards and downwards where the rock formations are thought to have been located.

The Munster and South Munster Basins

This inset map shows the outline of the Munster Basin in yellow. This was a major sedimentary basin, which was initiated in the middle of the Devonian Period or earlier, at least 380 million years ago. The basin accumulated in excess of 8km thickness of sediment. Towards the end of the Devonian, the South Munster Basin developed as a sub-basin where subsidence became greater than the area to the north known as the North Munster Shelf. Much of the sediment which infilled the basins was derived from high mountainous areas lying to the west, north and northeast.

Palinspastic model of the South Munster Basin

The inset map on the next page shows what the actual shape of the South Munster Basin might have been at the time of its infilling. Remember that the basin

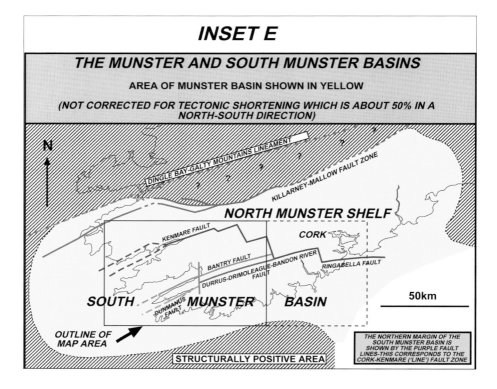

infill was shortened by about 50% at the end of the Carboniferous due to tectonic forces from the south. This tectonic event resulted in a radical change in the shape of the basin. This map attempts to reconstruct its original shape by

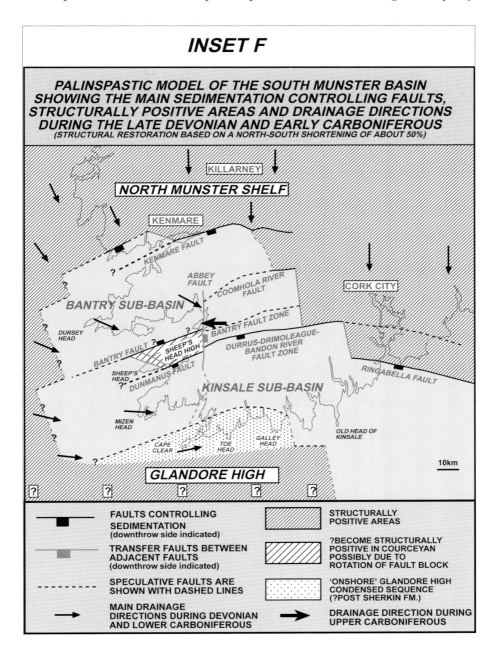

INSET F

PALINSPASTIC MODEL OF THE SOUTH MUNSTER BASIN SHOWING THE MAIN SEDIMENTATION CONTROLLING FAULTS, STRUCTURALLY POSITIVE AREAS AND DRAINAGE DIRECTIONS DURING THE LATE DEVONIAN AND EARLY CARBONIFEROUS
(STRUCTURAL RESTORATION BASED ON A NORTH-SOUTH SHORTENING OF ABOUT 50%)

KILLARNEY

NORTH MUNSTER SHELF

KENMARE

KENMARE FAULT

?

ABBEY FAULT

COOMHOLA RIVER FAULT

CORK CITY

BANTRY SUB-BASIN

DURSEY HEAD

BANTRY FAULT ZONE

?

SHEEP'S HEAD HIGH

DURRUS-DRIMOLEAGUE-BANDON RIVER FAULT ZONE

BANTRY FAULT ?

SHEEP'S HEAD

DUNMANUS FAULT

RINGABELLA FAULT

KINSALE SUB-BASIN

MIZEN HEAD

CAPE CLEAR

TOE HEAD

GALLEY HEAD

OLD HEAD OF KINSALE

10km

GLANDORE HIGH

? ? ? ? ?

	FAULTS CONTROLLING SEDIMENTATION (downthrow side indicated)		STRUCTURALLY POSITIVE AREAS
	TRANSFER FAULTS BETWEEN ADJACENT FAULTS (downthrow side indicated)		?BECOME STRUCTURALLY POSITIVE IN COURCEYAN POSSIBLY DUE TO ROTATION OF FAULT BLOCK
	SPECULATIVE FAULTS ARE SHOWN WITH DASHED LINES		'ONSHORE' GLANDORE HIGH CONDENSED SEQUENCE (?POST SHERKIN FM.)
	MAIN DRAINAGE DIRECTIONS DURING DEVONIAN AND LOWER CARBONIFEROUS		DRAINAGE DIRECTION DURING UPPER CARBONIFEROUS

unfolding the rock layers. It is important to note that the coastline as we see it today did not exist in the past. It is put in here for reference purposes only. Note that the reconstruction has resulted in the stretching of the coastline by 50% in a north-south direction. The map also shows a number of important faults, which are thought to have controlled the development of the basin.

Tectonic interpretation

At the lower left of the main map is an interpretation of a deep seismic survey across the Munster and South Munster Basins. The results clearly show the presence of the basin fills in yellow and the underlying "basement". The study has modeled a buried granite body, which underlies part of the Iveragh Peninsula area. This body is probably the southwesterly extension of the Leinster Granite.

Summary map

And finally, the Summary Map is located on the lower right hand corner of the map and shows the distribution of the rock layers on the basis of their interpreted environments instead of their composition. It also depicts the major fold axes, which include anticlines and synclines.

Conclusion

A map of this kind is like an historical manuscript. The rock layers amounting to over 8km in thickness are like the pages of the manuscript. Each layer records events and environments which existed millions of years in the past. The sequence of layers records the changing environments in the past. Once there was a sedimentary basin in this area in which sediments accumulated. They were later deformed, uplifted and fractured. They were then eroded down to the present day land surface. The map shows the outcrop of the deformed sediment layers on this surface.

   The map is a model which depicts the current understanding of the history of this sedimentary basin, its structure and outcrop pattern. Further research will inevitably refine this model and through the use of new techniques will almost certainly come up with interesting new perspectives on the geology of the region.

For further reading

"New Perspectives on the Old Red Sandstone," edited by P. F. Friend and B. P. J. Williams (London: Geological Society of London, 2000); "Sheet 24 Geology of West Cork," by

MacCarthy, Sleeman and Pracht (Dublin: Geological Survey of Ireland, 2001); "A Geological Description of West Cork and Adjacent Parts to Accompany the Bedrock Geology 1:100,000 Scale Map Series, Sheet 24: West Cork," by Sleeman and Pracht (Dublin: Geological Survey of Ireland, 2002); and "Geology of the Devonian-Carboniferous South Munster Basin, Ireland," by MacCarthy (Cork: University College, Cork, 2004).

15

Two Pages from the *Book of Kells*
Jennifer O'Reilly

One of the principal tools of the history of art is *iconography,* the study of symbols and narratives in visual art. As a method, iconography can be demanding and exact. The art historian Erwin Panofsky pictured "iconographical analysis" as leading to a more general understanding of culture, historical processes, and "intrinsic meaning."

This brief note gives the flavour of an iconographical analysis: it is a kind of close reading, bent on precision and thoroughness. It also hints at the wider reading of the manuscript's significance.

Introduction

Insular gospel books, which were also precious liturgical objects, characteristically apply motifs from the traditions of Celtic and Saxon fine metalwork to the decoration of the written word, most notably in display scripts at the opening of the sacred text. In the *Book of Kells* the native repertoire of abstract ornament (curvilinear patterns of trumpets, petals and spirals; rectilinear fret and step patterns; ribbon and zoomorphic interlace; highly stylised animals) is combined with imports from the representational art of the Mediterranean world, such as vine scrolls, lions, peacocks and human figures.

Different categories of ornament, which are clearly defined and separated as if within the cell-walls of a piece of precious metalwork in other Insular gospel books, occasionally overspill their boundaries in the *Book of Kells.* The framing bands which outline the individual letter forms and delineate their panels of ornament also help unify the whole design by their color and line.

Folio 29

The first page of St Matthew's gospel (folio 29 in the manuscript, shown on the next page) bears only two words, *Liber generationis,* yet is almost illegible. The

circular bosses, curves and spinning spirals of *Liber* are counterpoised by the rectangular multiple frames holding *generationis*. The first syllable, *Lib*, forms a sweeping ligature which spans the entire page, its last letter encircling the second syllable, *er.*

Below, the shrunken word *gene/rati/onis* is divided into three lines with letter forms of almost runic obscurity; two lines are shown in orange letters on purple and the centre line in purple on orange.

This display script, in which text dissolves and becomes image, has been described as sacred calligraphy. Discerning the form of the words, whose letters are distorted in shape and relative size and veiled by the ornament, provides some visual analogy to the monastic practice of *lectio divina* in which the reader meditatively seeks the spiritual meaning concealed beneath the literal text of the Scriptures.

Significance of the page

Matthew 1:1-17, beginning with the words *Liber generationis* (the Book of the Generation, or Genealogy), records Christ's human lineage from the royal house of Judah. The following verse begins the account of the incarnation, which stresses Christ's divine as well as his human nature. Patristic and Insular biblical commentators customarily linked the account of Christ's human birth and consequent mortality announced in Matthew 1:18 with his identification as the divine Creator at the opening of John's gospel. The text begins with Christ's name, in which commentators believed his identity was symbolically made known. It is a characteristic feature of Insular gospel books that they embellish the opening of this text to equal or even surpass the decorated opening of the gospel itself.

Folio 34

In the *Book of Kells* folio 34, shown at the beginning of this Chapter only the first three words of Matthew 1:18 are shown: *Christi autem (h) generatio.* The second and third words are written in Insular majuscule script and lie almost unnoticed at the bottom of the page (see the detail on the next page). The first word, *Christi,* is shown through the customary form XP, derived from the Greek letters *chi* and *rho*, which are the first two letters of the Greek title Christ (Messiah, "the Anointed One").

The Kells artist has transformed this ancient pictorial convention of abbreviation of the sacred name so that the initial letter embraces the whole page. The four curved arms of the *chi* radiate from a great central lozenge and terminate in spools of Celtic spirals and roundels; the much smaller letter *rho* and the Latin ending "i" stem from extensions of an equilateral cross. A foreshortened diagonal version of this golden cross appears in the rhombus or lozenge at the heart of the *chi*.

Details

The page teems with life. It is inhabited by creatures of earth, air and water: within the lozenge, an image of the quadripartite cosmos, are four tiny human figures; to the left of the *chi* are moths and angels and at the bottom of the page are cats and mice and a black otter with a fish in its jaws. Even the interlace ornament is formed from vine scrolls and stylised birds, serpents, quadrupeds and humans.

The decoration of the text of Christ's birth suggests the identification of Christ incarnate with Christ the Creator-Logos. Christ as the divine Word is here revealed in a word, in a single letter, concealed within the design. Similarly, commentators meditating on his name at this point in Matthew's gospel, described his divinity as lying hidden in his creation, beneath his human flesh at his incarnation and beneath the literal letter of the scriptural text.

What would be next?

A student of Insular manuscripts would study a wide range of images like these, to build a sense of why they were made, how they developed, and what they signified. Images in art history are rarely studied in isolation, even though they are sometimes shown that way in galleries.

For further reading

Bernard Meehan, *An Illustrated Introduction to the Manuscript in Trinity College, Dublin* (London: Thames and Hudson, 1994); Carol Ann Farr, *The Book of Kells: Its Function and Audience* (London: British Library, 1997).

16

A High Resolution, Mutichannel Aerial Photograph

Jim McGrath

This is a digital photograph of an area around the University College Cork in Ireland. The image is a composite, made up of a black and white image overlaid with a digital elevation model (DEM) that is colored, in the language of cartography, "according to an elevation look-up-table." Two scales from the look-up table are inset to give a qualitative idea of the color range.

This is no ordinary aerial photograph, but a complicated product of multiple cameras and digital processing. It is an intriguing example of a photographic technology that produces *more information* than can be seen at any given moment.

The camera

The camera used to take this image is called the High Resolution Stereo Camera-Airborne (HRSC-A). In use, the camera is mounted on the bottom of a plane.

Nine lenses

The onboard camera has nine distinct CCD (charge-coupled device) lines. Four of the lines are designed to provide multi-spectral information. To achieve this, they are each filtered differently to respond to (a) three color regions of the visible spectrum (red, green and blue) and (b) the near infrared thermal band, labelled *nIR*.

The five remaining lines (see illustrations on the next page) are configured to capture panchromatic (full-color) images at angles of +20.5°, -20.5°, +12°, -12°

The resolution of the camera itself allows a 15 cm pixel size for the Nadir Panchromatic channel and 30 cm pixel size for the other eight channels.

The photo at the bottom of the preceding page gives an indication of the minimum scale of discernable features. The university library is at the centre. Cars are clearly visible, and people are milling in front of the student café and sitting on the green in front of the humanities building.

Digital elevation model

Often images like these can be useful as-is, or they can be given false colors to bring out features of the landscape. In other cases, however, what is needed is quantitative information.

The stereo perspective viewing channels may be analysed to produce a Digital Elevation Model of the study area. The German Aerospace Agency (DLR) has provided an extremely robust, high-resolution DEM that offers a horizontal resolution of 1 meter with elevation values expressed to the nearest 10 cm.

It is possible to re-analyze the stereo images to produce a DEM with different properties. Known as "stereo matching," the method estimates depth by measuring the relative location of the same feature or pattern in two perspective images. This matching may be achieved by, for example, computing a Sum of Absolute Difference or by statistical correlation between two or more perspective images. The simpler "SAD" formula, which searches for the disparity at which the difference between two image regions is minimised, is this —

$$sad[disp] = \sum_{r=-\frac{R}{2}}^{\frac{R}{2}} \sum_{c=-\frac{C}{2}}^{\frac{C}{2}} leftimage[r][c] - rightimage[r][c + disp].$$

— where the indices (r,c) are the addresses of the pixels in each image, r is the row of the image analysis window, c is the column of the image analysis window, R is the total number of rows in the image analysis window, C is the total number of columns in the image analysis window and "*disp*" is the disparity or parallax — the distance by which the analysis window has moved in the right image relative to that in the left image.

Producing a digital elevation model

Before we show the results of these analyses, here is another application of the same technology. The photo on the next page is an anaglyphic image of part of the campus of the university. An anaglyph is a stereo image printed so that one eye sees a red image, and the other a green image. (The next two photos are the constituent red and green images for the anaglyph.) If you have a pair of ana-

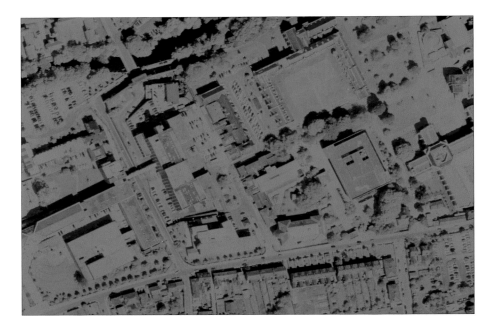

glyph-viewing glasses — one eye with a red lens, the other one blue — you should see three dimensions in the image. (Glasses can also be made with transparent sheets of colored plastic film.)

Anaglyphs have a long history, and they used to be drawn by hand before photography. Mathematicians, architects, and engineers have used them to visualize difficult structures. In 2003, the European Space Agency's Mars Express entered orbit and began sending back similar anaglyph images of the Martian suface which may be viewed on the ESA website.

Anaglyphs are more sensitive to the viewer's position than ordinary photographs. If you have anaglyphic glasses, try moving your head as you look at the image. The buildings seem to shear: an illusion based on assumptions the brain makes about the relation between your eyes and the world.

Measuring elevation

These last two pictures show the result of of applying the SAD formula. They show, in close-up, the central quad of the university, with the library and student café. The idea is to tune the DEM to be sharper so that instantaneous changes in elevation are supported and the DEM's smoothing is reduced. This kind of image can be directly measured, and used to generate quantitative data.

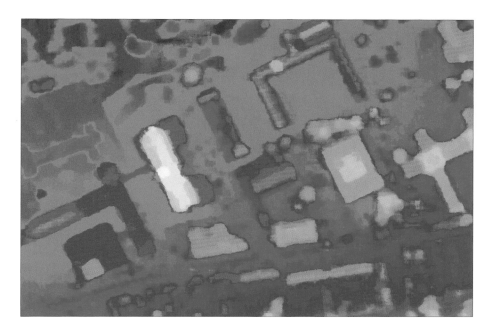

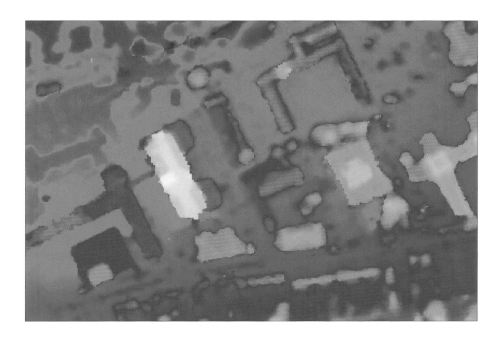

Using the data

A project, funded by Ordnance Survey Ireland, is underway at University College Cork to analyze the aerial photography, automatically identifying features such as roads and buildings to speed-up the map-making process. It is hoped that an improved DEM will augment this analysis.

Since 1998, a number of projects at the Department of Civil and Environmental Engineering, have exploited high-resolution DEMs in the hydrodynamic and hydrological modelling of the River Lee in Cork and the River Feale in North Kerry, an adjoining county in Ireland. Reliable high-resolution DEMs may also be used to accurately measure the quantity of material extracted or deposited at quarries and landfill sites.

For more information

Follow the European Space Agency's Mars Express programme and view stunning anaglyph images of Mars taken with the HRSC camera: www.esa.int/SPECIALS/Mars_Express/

Jim McGrath, Kevin Barry, Philip O'Kane, and Richard Kavanagh, UCC, "High Resolution DEM and Sea Level Rise in the Centre of Cork-Blue City Project," Impacts of Climate Change, Urban Hydrology: Stormwater Management, National Hydrology Seminar, 11th November 2003, Tullamore Court Hotel, Ireland; Luca Migliori, J. Philip O'Kane, "The Hydrology and Hydraulics of a Pumped Polder in North Kerry – A Case Study in Hydroinformatics," Modelling of Water Quality and Quantity, The Water Framework Directive: Monitoring and Modelling Issues for River Basin Management, National Hydrology Seminar, 16th November 2004, Tullamore Court Hotel, Ireland; John Martin, "Dewatering the Lower Feale Catchment: 'A Virtual Water World,'" Ph.D. Thesis, 2002, University College, Cork, Ireland; Gerhard Neukum and the HRSC-Team, Berlin, "The HRSC-AX cameras: evaluation of the technical concept and presentation of application results after one year of operation," *Photogrammetric Week '01,* edited by D. Fritsch and R. Spiller (Heidelberg: Wichmann, 2001), 117-31; F. Wewel, F. Scholten, G. Neukum, and L. Albertz, "Digitale Luftbildaufnahme mit der HRSC — Ein Schritt in die Zukunft der Photogrammetrie," *Photogrammetrie-Fernerkundung Geoinformation,* vol. 6 (Stuttgart: E. Schweizerbart'sche Verlagsbuchhandlung, 1993), 337-48. For *Viewing* image processing software: www.ermapper.com.

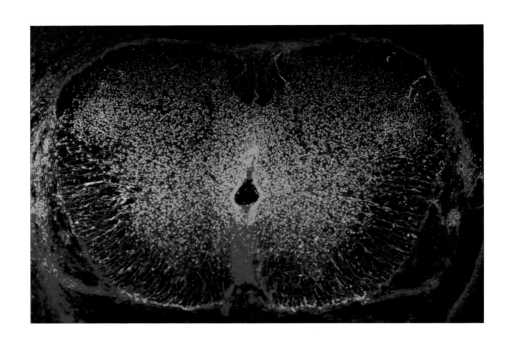

17

Fluorescence Microscopy of the Spinal Cord

Kieran Mc Dermott and Denis Barry

This is a study of the growth of the spinal cord, tracking the growth and distribution of three proteins: nestin; a protein abbreviated GFAP; and one called vimentin.

Confocal microscopy

In the course of the Study, we make use of several of the major techniques of contemporary light microscopy, including polarizing and fluorescence.

The technique used here is *confocal microscopy.* The microscope uses lasers to excite fluorophores ("labels" — chemicals that glow) in the specimen at selected levels. The microscope focuses on one layer at a time, collects the light from it, and moves on. The images are "stacked" to form a single image. That way the confocal microscope avoids a problem that plagues light microscopy — a very shallow depth of field.

The technique is very sensitive, and can be used on living tissues. The individual images are very faint (and very beautiful). Together they create an image unlike any conventional photograph — an image with potentially unlimited depth of field.

Gross atonomy

In the opening image, the spinal cord is shown in cross-section. The grey matter is at the center. Around the edges is the white matter, which appears darker here.

The colors

The grey matter is labelled with propidium iodide, which glows a livid magenta when it is illuminated by a yellow laser at 568nm. The protein vimentim appears as blue fibers, and the protein GFAP appears as green fibers, both in the white matter. The red areas show the presence of the label Cy5, which gloes when it is illuminated by a 647nm (far red) laser. The experiment uses three lasers simultaneously for red, green, and blue fluorescence.

The experiment

This is a high-magnification detail of part of a spinal cord. (Compare with the opening photo.) Here long fibers of the protein nestin appear stained an orangered. They can be seen coursing out of the grey matter of the spinal cord (at the left) and into the white matter.

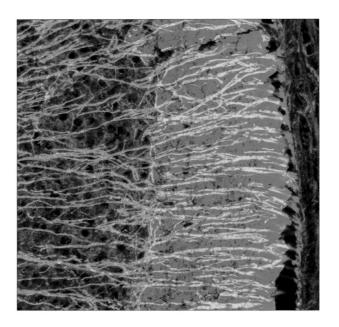

On the next page is another high-magnification image. Here we are interested to observe that the green fibers contain the protein GFAP, it seems to be originating from cell bodies, which glow blue because they are labeled with propidium iodide. And as before, the red fibers contain the protein vimentin, and glow red because they are labeled with Cy5.

Strength and limitations of confocal microscopy

The technique is limited in several ways: confocal microscopy is time consuming and expensive, and the lasers tend to bleach the fluorescent dyes in the specimen.

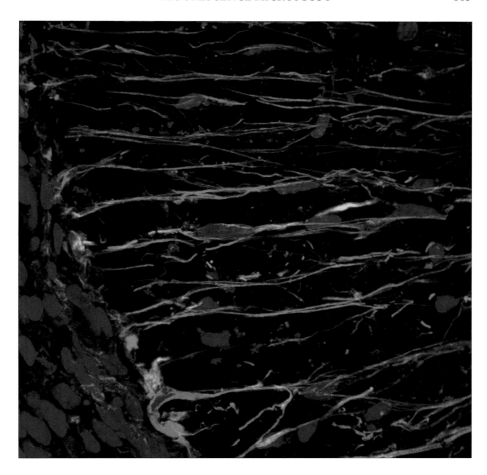

Otherwise the technique is perfectly adequate to its purpose: the high resolution and spectacular clarity offered by confocal microscopy, combined with multi-antibody labeling methods, allows a four-dimensional reconstruction of the dynamic processes occurring in the developing spinal cord.

Confocal microscopy presents pictures in "false color," and it presents single pictures that are actually composites of many images. The same is true in a number of fields (see Chapter 16, for example, where the subject is aerial photographs). Confocal microscopes are one of a group of electron- and light-microscope technologies whose purpose is to enhance the contrast of thin, translucent organic materials. Chapter 21 lists some others, and electron-microscope techniques are described in chapter 27. Together these technologies comprise a group of allied practices, with common elements and overlapping strategies for image production and interpretation (see the Introduction for the full form of this argument).

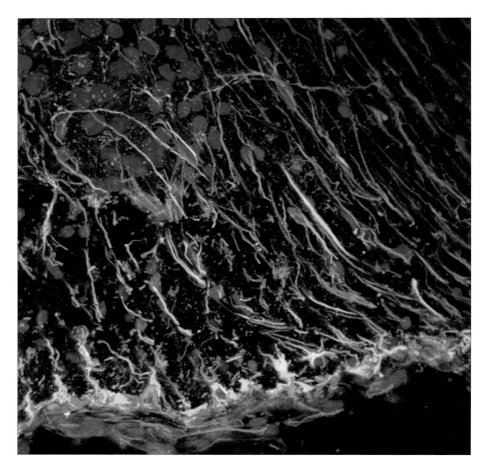

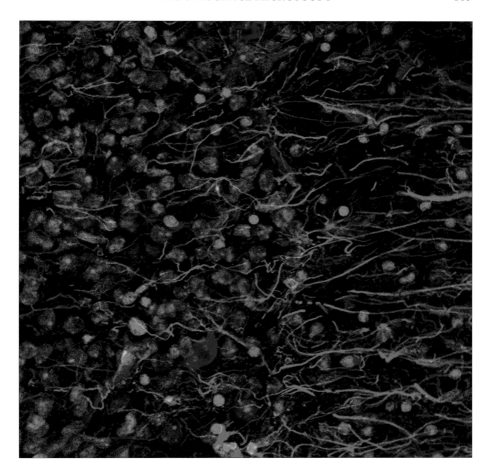

For further reading

S.C. Noctor, A.C. Flint, et al, "Neurons Derived From Radial Glial Cells Establish Radial Units In The Neocortex," *Nature* (February 8, 2002): 714-720; M. Oudega and E. Marini, "Expression of Vimentin and Glial Fibrillary Acidic Protein in the Developing Rat Spinal Cord: An Immunocytochemical Study of the Spinal Cord Glial System," *Journal of Anatomy* 179 (December 1991): 97-114; H.Y. Yang, N. Lieska, et al., "Immunotyping Of Radial Glia and Their Glial Derivatives During Development of The Rat Spinal Cord," *Journal of Neurocytology* 22 no. 7 (July 1993): 558-71; G. Chanas-Sacre et al., "Radial Glia Phenotype: Origin, Regulation, and Transdifferentiation," *Journal of Neuroscience Research* 61 no. 4 (August 15, 2000): 357-63; Barry and McDermott, "Differentiation of Radial Glia From Radial Precursor Cells and Transformation into Astrocytes in The Developing Rat Spinal Cord," *Glia* (Jan 28, 2005). For light- and electron microscope techniques in this context, see Elkins, *Six Stories from the End of Representation* (Stanford: Stanford University Press, 2007)

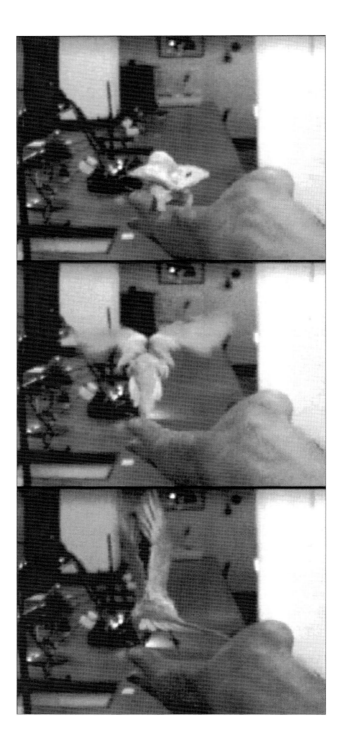

18

Ground Effect and Bird Flight
Marc Shorten

These frames are from a test film, part of an experiment to determine how bird flight works when the bird is close to a surface like water (or a table). The phenomenon under study, *ground effect* (GE), causes a wing to experience increased lift and decreased induced drag when it flies close to a surface. For GE to occur flight altitude must be on the order of one wingspan or less over a surface; the effect is often best exploited over calm water because of its smoothness relative to land.

The effect on different birds

Large sea-birds (Phalacrocoracidae, for example cormorants and shags), pelicans (Pelicanidae), albatrosses (Diomedeidae) and many species of waterfowl (for instance Eider duck, which are Anatidae, *Somateria mollissima*) regularly fly in ground effect to reduce locomotion costs. Little work has been done to compare GE flight behaviour or aerodynamics between species.

Induced drag

The largest component of GE is a reduction in *induced drag*, the slowing force associated with lift production, i.e. staying airborne). Exploiting GE is particularly beneficial for large birds because induced drag increases with the square of mass. For example, when a wing is 0.22 wingspans above a smooth substrate only about 25% of normal induced drag is experienced. This drag reduction is primarily as a result of decreased downwash off the wing, as air is forced parallel to the ground and the formation of wing-tip vortices is disrupted.

This project involves field observations using standard and high-speed digital video. Proportional numbers of flights observed in and out of GE are calculated from these data for a variety of species. These data are examined in the light of morphological and environmental data associated with the behavioural observations.

Measuring the birds' wings

This is a wing-tracing of a male Peregrine Falcon (*Falco peregrinus*).

The tracing is saved as a Bitmap file and scaled down in size to allow it to be viewed in totality on the screen. Then the picture is opened in an image analysis package (*Scion Image* Beta Version 4.02) so that the wing area can be measured. (More on why we're doing this in a moment.)

The initial task is to set the scale so that a given number of pixels corresponds to a given number of centimeters. This is achieved by drawing a line along a known distance on the wing (in this case, 16cm, the width of the wing where it meets the bird's body). The software automatically gauges the length of the line in pixels and thus, when the user tells it how to, the software converts pixels to centimeters.

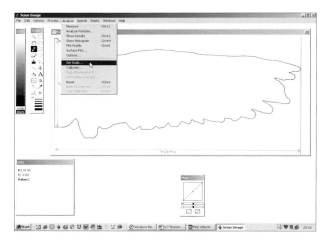

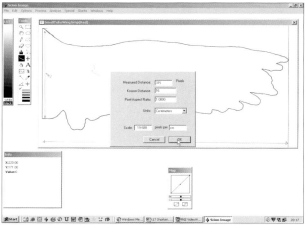

Once this is done, the picture must be cleaned of extraneous detail that the software could mistakenly regard as relevant. This is done by erasing everything in the picture except the outline of the wing. To further simplify the image the image is converted to a binary format where everything is either black or white (Bottom photo).

Using the magic wand tool the outline of the wing and nothing else is selected. Using the Measure function on the software, the area of the outline is then simply read from the screen. The cursor points to this in the photo on the next page. Knowing the full wingspan of the bird, the area of both wings and the section of body in between is easily calculated. Adding all of these together gives the total lift-producing wing area. This is one of the most important characteristics of a bird's flight anatomy.

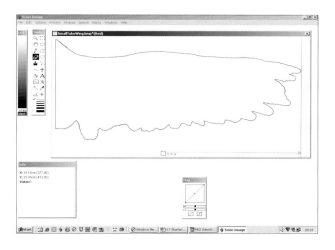

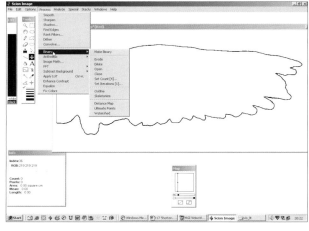

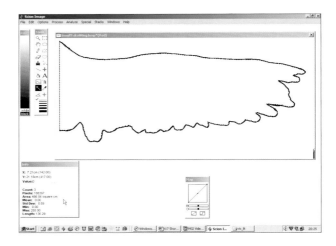

Videos in the lab

The Budgerigar (*Melopsittacus undulatus, a kind of parakat*) was studied in the laboratory. A high-speed video camera recorded its flight. (The three frames shown here were a test flight, made to see how the camera worked. The result was lovely, unquantifiable footage, which flickers like an old Lumière Brothers film.)

The use of reference nodes (shown on the next page as red dots) allows demarcation of identifiable body parts in each frame. This, in turn, means that descriptions of flight behaviour may be brought beyond the verbal, using mathematics and coordinate geometry to make description more robust and less subjective. Each frame here is only 0.004 seconds in duration.

The footage is filmed with a grid in the background as a measure of the scale. In the computer, relevant parts of the bird's body are assigned colored nodes (they are red in the video). In this example, the nodes are the wing-tip, the carpal bend (the "wrist" of the wing) and the eye. In the video loop it's possible to see, for example, how when slowed down the top and the bottom of the wingbeat sequence may be compared with ease and accuracy. This is done by superimposing one image of the bird over a previous image. Given that the eye's reference node doesn't move relative to the rest of the body, the superimposition can be done by lining up the eye in the two pictures.

Each frame of the video is studied using node coordinates, allowing the motion of the nodes to be graphed.

Quantifying flight

The nodes are used to measure several things: wingbeat frequencies, wingbeat amplitudes, and whole-body air-speeds.

In this example, the coordinates of the nodes are used to estimate the bird's speed in meters per second (ms[-1]), the vertical displacement of the wing-tip in meters (m) and the frequency of the wingbeat in hertz (Hz).

The image below shows shows x and y coordinates for body parts of the bird during a flight sequence captured on video. Thus, from only 0.072 seconds of video we know this bird flew at 6.85ms[-1], with a wingbeat amplitude of 0.36m and a wingbeat frequency of 19.23Hz.

In themselves, these curves allow a geometric representation of the main characteristics of this sequence of bird flight. In the broader scheme of things such graphs allow comparisons of different birds, or even the same bird under different conditions such as changes in air temperature, air pressure or wind speed, or even factors like body mass, wing shape etc. There are established mathematical models of expected flight behaviour based on anatomical measurements such as those outlined above.

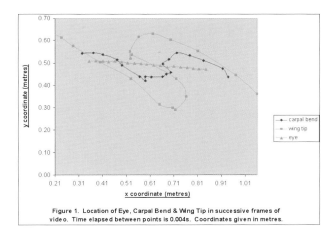

Figure 1. Location of Eye, Carpal Bend & Wing Tip in successive frames of video. Time elapsed between points is 0.004s. Coordinates given in metres.

Ground flight modelling

The ground effect modelling here was developed using behavioral, morphological and experimental data, as well as the bird-flight aeronautical theory and programs of Colin Pennycuick. This software makes it possible to compare actual observations of speed and wingbeat frequency with the expected figures for a species in ground effect. The software has been developed in such a way that it can be modified as the data are refined in the course of the research.

For further reading

Colin Pennycuick, *Bird Flight Performance: A Practical Calculation Manual* (Oxford: Oxford University Press, 1989); Pennycuick, *Measuring Birds' Wings for Flight Performance Calculations*, second edition (Bristol: Boundary Layer Publications, 1999); see also www.ucc.ie/research/mshorten.

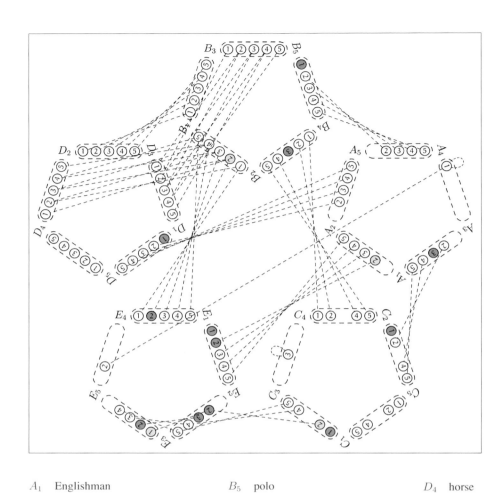

A_1	Englishman	B_5	polo	D_4	horse
A_2	Spaniard	C_1	coffee	D_5	zebra
A_3	Irishman	C_2	tea	E_1	red
A_4	Nigerian	C_3	milk	E_2	green
A_5	Japanese	C_4	orange juice	E_3	ivory
B_1	go	C_5	Guinness	E_4	yellow
B_2	cricket	D_1	dog	E_5	blue
B_3	judo	D_2	snails		
B_4	poker	D_3	fox		

19

Solving the "Zebra Problem"

Marc Van Dongen

The problem, which may have originated with Lewis Carroll, is this:

> There are five houses of different colors,
> inhabited by people from different nations,
> with different pets,
> different drinks, and
> different sports.

There are fourteen more clues:

1. The Englishman lives in the red house.
2. The Spaniard owns a dog.
3. The man in the green house drinks coffee.
4. The Irishman drinks tea.
5. The green house is to the right of the ivory house.
6. The Go player owns snails.
7. The man in the yellow house plays cricket.
8. The guy in the house in the middle drinks milk.
9. The Nigerian lives in the first house.
10. The judo player lives next to the man who has a fox.
11. The cricketer lives next to the man who has a horse.
12. The poker player drinks orange juice.
13. The Japanese plays polo.
14. The Nigerian lives next to the blue house.

The question is:

> Who owns the zebra and who drinks Guinness?

The technique

It's a textbook problem for computer science students taking logic programming, constraint satisfaction, or artificial intelligence. In the exhibition that preceded this book, the solution was given in a PowerPoint presentation, involving fifty steps.

The fifty slides — some of them shown here — almost completely mimicked what a constraint-based solver (on a computer) would do, without images, in order to solve this problem. An important ingredient of such solvers is that they use the constraint between the variables in the problems, together with simple

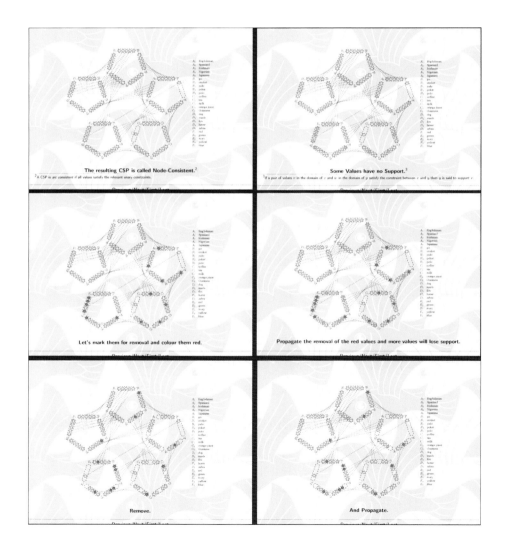

reasoning, to remove values from the domains of the variables that cannot participate to a solution. This process is easy to visualize in a picture, even for large problems.

(There are several limitations imposed by the fact that this is a book. Films, such as those of birds in flight — as in Chapter 18 — are an obvious example. Less apparent is the fact that books can only have a limited number of illustrations; in that case the consequence is that this solution cannot be shown, but only conjured. Another, subtler, limitation is the resolution and accuracy of the printing on the page, which affects high-resolution and high-accuracy projects such as those in Chapters 11 and 16.)

Graphical and non-graphical in mathematics

Since the generation of Descartes, there have been debates in mathematics over the use of visual images. In the seventeenth century, simple algebraic equations were sometimes not considered solved unless the equations were accompanied by a picture. Thus a quadratic equation would have to be accompanied by a sketch of a conic section and a line, which showed the answer graphically. This was known as the "construction of equations."

The advent of calculus at the turn of the century also allowed scholars to easily and accurately sketch graphs of complicated functions.

The abandonment of the image

In nineteenth-century mathematics, the tendency was to mistrust images in favor of equations. Mathematicians began finding examples of pathological functions in calculus — functions that could not be drawn but were important to theoretical conjectures (for example, Weierstrass's everywhere-continuous, nowhere-differentiable function).

There were exceptions, such as John Venn's interest in logic diagrams, based on the work of Leonhard Euler, and plaster models of mathematical functions. In the last thirty years, with the advent of computers, images have come back into favor — they are used, for example, in combinatoric problems (Ramsey theory), in the topology of minimal surfaces, in knot theory, and in fractal geometry.

Images as heuristic and pedagogic tools

In the end, however, images are not used to prove theorems in mathematics. They can guide a student's understanding, help give an intuitive feel for a problem, and show off the difficulty or beauty of a proof: but they are not, in themselves, proofs.

Even this Zebra problem is not really a proof: it is a representation of a logical deduction. And yet there is more to the story, because once a mathematician becomes convinced that a graphical strategy works, then he or she may choose to work problems using pictures alone.

(And how did Dodgson solve his own puzzle? Probably with a picture — from which he could have deduced the underlying logic.)

Drawing these pictures

As you can imagine the pictures are difficult to draw using a computer graphics package. Indeed, the pictures were drawn using a little metapost program. (Metapost is a language for specifying pictures. It is closely related to Don Knuth's metafont.)

It is typical of the new interest in graphical solutions that the pictures are drawn by computer. In this case, they did not *have* to be: but in most cases, including fractal geometry, there is no alternative.

For further reading

John Venn, *Symbolic Logic* (London: MacMillan and Co., 1881); Henk Bos, *Lectures on the History of Mathematics* (Providence, Rhode Island: American Mathematical Society, 1993), chapter 2, "The Concept of Construction and the Representation of Curves in Seventeenth-century Mathematics"; for Metapost, see csweb.ucc.ie/~dongen/mpost/mpost.html.

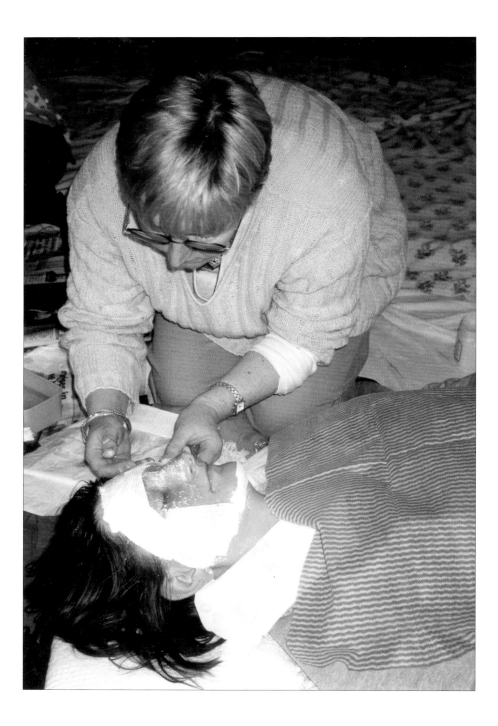

20

Masks in Social Work

Nuala Lordan, Mary Wilson, Deirdre Quirke

The use of maskmaking as a tool in social work education offers opportunities and poses new challenges for addressing post modern dilemmas of uncertainty, chaos and crises that are everyday events in the lives of social workers and service users. Social workers in training learn to acknowledge the equality of cognitive and intuitive processes and endeavor to integrate them in an inclusive practice pedagogy. The practice of making of the mask requires the completion of a number of tasks involving the action, reflection, dialogue and action cycle and it is through this experiential learning that this practice wisdom is developed.

Choosing a partner

Following a relaxation exercise, participants choose a partner with whom to make a mask. One lies prostrate, the other kneels as they apply the materials. Trust building is a central component of the exercise.

Making the mask

It is important that the person lies down: it changes the relationship between the two. This position is a symbolic representation of the powerlessness and dependency frequently experienced by service users.

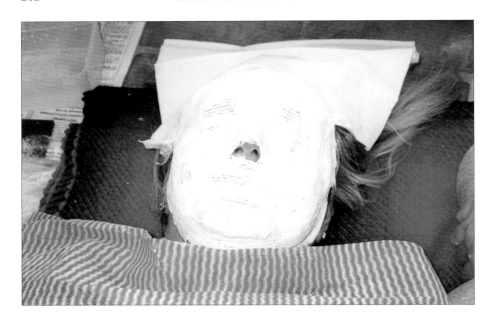

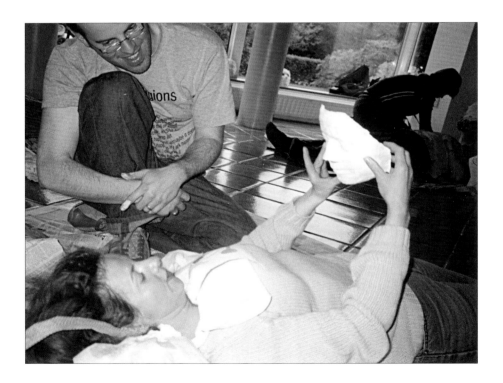

"Birthing" the mask

The "birthing" of the mask, that is when it is taken off the face, is usually an exciting and sacred event. Participants find that the experience connects with deep wellsprings of emotion. For both men and women it has frequent resonance with the life theme.

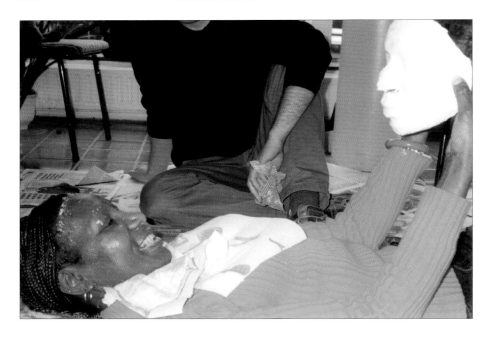

Reflections on the process

Next participants are requested to engage in a reflective exercise where they dialogue and document their reactions to the process. To translate learning from the maskmaking, questions are provided which guide the learner along the route to connect with universal themes.

Painting the mask

The penultimate stage involves participants painting their masks, which when dry are ready for the performance. Much dialogue takes place as a result of revisiting their experiences, thus furthering and deepening the process of reflection. As a result new knowledge of self and the other begin to emerge.

Dialogue and evaluation

The finale involves presenting of each participant's mask to the other using the medium of performance. Participants dress the mask for presentation using colorful materials. This is followed by a performance or a play of the mask that is made, using mime, song, dance or words. This culminates with the presentation of the mask to each other. Symbolically and figuratively this actualizes the concepts of giving and receiving.

Ends of the exercise

The maskmaking experience provides students with an opportunity to explore the process of giving and receiving within the context of social groupwork and to develop greater awareness of self and other.

The process is limited by the voluntary nature of participation. Maskmaking cannot be a compulsory or core teaching unit, because the students are exposed to the risk of encountering both the familiar and the strange within themselves and the other. Participants get different things from the experience, depending on their levels of self-awareness and commitment to the process.

For further reading

P. Freire, *The Pedagogy of the Oppressed* (New York: Herder and Herder, 1970); D. Kolb, *Experiential Learning* (Englewood Cliffs, NJ: Prentice Hall, 1984); N. Lordan, M. Wilson, and D. Quirke, "Breaking the mould: Maskmaking as an 'inclusive' Educational Tool," in *Life's Rich Pattern: Cultural Diversity and the Education of Adults,* edited by J. Jones and G. Normie. Papers from the 7th International Conference on Adult Education and the Arts, Glasgow, Scotland, July 2002; O. Luedemann, "Interacting Productively with the Familiar and the Strange", in *Fromm Forum* (Heidelberg: International Fromm Society, 2003).

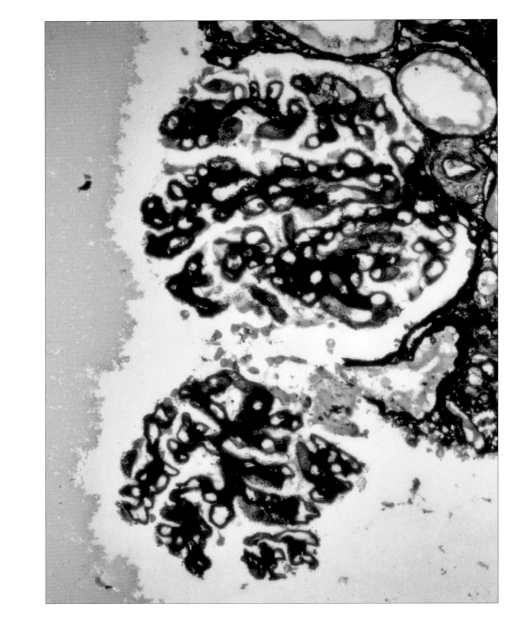

21

Diagnosis of Membranous Glomerulopathy by Kidney Biopsy

Nollaig Parfrey

Nephrotic syndrome develops when damage to the kidneys leads to loss of protein in the urine. It is associated with diabetes, but has many other causes. The commonest cause of nephrotic syndrome in adults is membranous glomerulopathy.

The diagnosis of membranous glomerulopathy is not straightforward and is not made based on a single feature. It is complex, and utilises the complementary techniques of light microscopy, fluorescence microscopy and electron microscopy. A definite diagnosis requires a biopsy of the kidney.

The anatomy

To read the images, it is necessary to briefly review the relevant anatomy.

Glomeruli selectively filter waste from the blood and produce urine which is then sent to the bladder. They are round structures scattered throughout the kidneys. They are largely made up of small blood vessels named capillary loops. A capillary loop consists of a blood vessel lined by endothelial cells which lie on a basement membrane; the basement membrane is lined on its other side by epithelial cells. Thus, the basement membrane is the meat in the sandwich between endothelial cells and epithelial cells.

Membranous glomerulopathy is an autoimmune disease linked to susceptibility genes and caused by autoantibodies to an autoantigen in the kidneys. This leads to formation of immune deposits in the glomerular basement membrane under the epithelial cells. The basement membrane grows up around the immune deposits.

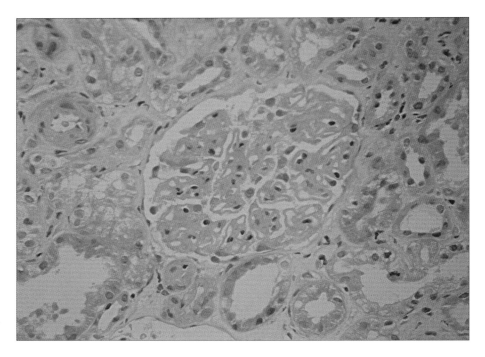

Haematoxylin and eosin

Haematoxylin and eosin (H&E) is a common stain in light microscopy (photo above). The haematoxylin is a base, and stains things blue; eosin, the "counter-stain," is acidic, and stains things red. Effectively, it makes a colorful "picture" out of otherwise translucent tissues. Here H&E staining reveals diffuse thickening of capillary loops in the glomerulus. The capillary loops appear thickened because the basement membrane is thickened.

Silver staining

Silver staining is another common technique in light microscopy (see the top image on the next page).

   Here a silver stain of a glomerulus shows multiple little spikes of silver-positive black material. The silver spikes are not the immune deposits but rather spikes of basement membrane that grow around the immune deposits.

Immunofluorescence

Immunofluorescence microscopy is a more sophisticated technique in light microscopy (see the bottom image on the next page). Fluorescent dyes are attached by antigen-antibody binding to molecules of interest present in the tissue.

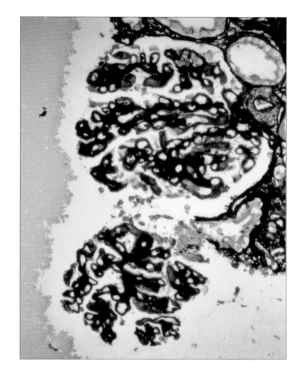

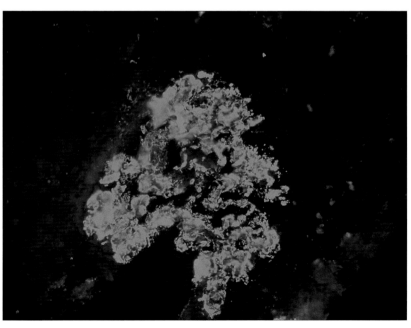

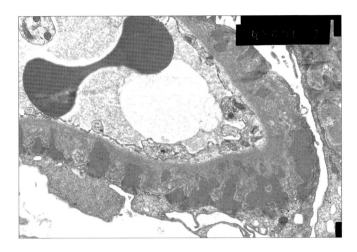

In this case, this immunofluorescence image of a single glomerulus shows strong diffuse positive green immunostaining using a fluorescein-labelled antibody directed against immunoglobulin G; it reveals immunoglobulin G deposits in a peripheral capillary loop pattern.

Electron microscopy

Transmission electron microscopy (photo above) is used for very high magnification at the cellular and subcellular level to examine features that are not visible at the light microscopic level. Here multiple electron-dense immune deposits (black) are seen in the basement membrane under the epithelial cells.

Conclusions

In this case, we see diffuse thickening of capillary loops, silver spikes, and immunoglobulin G deposition; these immune deposits are shown to be subepithelial. The combination of clinical findings (protein in the urine and reduced protein in the blood) and light, immunofluorescence, and electron microscopic findings establish the diagnosis of membranous glomerulopathy.

No one of these techniques is sufficient in itself, and each one requires extensive experience to develop confidence in dealing with subtle changes. The diagnosis is therefore a combination of multiple imaging technologies and visual skills that are obtained slowly from experience of many cases. Few images yield relatively straightforward visual criteria (such as the spikes in the silver stained sample); most require qualitative assessments and extensive comparisons of similar cases. In that sense, the material presented here is necessarily a less adequate representation of its subject than most other chapters in this book.

For further reading

Renal Pathology with Clinical and Functional Correlations, second edition, edited by C.G. Tisher and B.M. Brenner (Philadelphia: Lippincott, Williams, and Wilkins,1994); *Heptinstall's Pathology of the Kidney,* fifth edition, J.C. Jennette et al. (Philadelphia: Lippincott-Raven, 1998); *Robbins and Cotran Pathologic Basis of Disease*, seventh edition, edited by V. Kumar, A.K. Abbas, and N. Fausto (Philadelphia: Elsevier Saunders, 2005).

22

A Virtual Archive of Inscribed Stones

Orla Murphy, Elisabeth Okasha, Thierry Daubos, and Dáibhí Ó Cróinín

Here a team uses a laser scanner to capture the surface of an inscribed stone in the field at Toureen Peacaun, Ireland, Co. Tipperary. The scanner collects a *point cloud,* a set of points at known *x, y, z* locations in space. The resulting digital file is comprised of voxels (3-D pixels) in the computer. It can be used to machine three-dimensional replicas for study and exhibition; and it is also useful for checking contentious interpretations, or — most generally — for preserve monuments for the future. As a "point cloud," the stone can easily be disseminated on the internet.

The object

In this case, the team began with a positive cast of an inscription on a high cross shaft at Toureen Peacaun. The cast is shown at right; an old photograph of the actual monument is reproduced toward the end of this essay.

The 3-D scan

This is the same object, in the 3-D model. The blue color is just one of the default textures available in the software (called Rapidform) to visualize the model using shaded rendering.

What seems to be a continuous blue surface — it would be pixels in a digital image, or particles of dye in a photograph — is a set of linked points in space. In this model the inscribed area is 37.4 cm x 73.4 cm height, and it is actually comprised of linked points in space, like a Buckminster Fuller lattice. This one has 411,000 vertices and 821,000 triangles.

The nominal resolution is 1mm, but in practice, because of the need to collate "point clouds" of voxels from individual scans, and to filter the results, the effective resolution is 1.3 mm.

The inscription captured in the computer

Now the image is under the operator's control. It is possible to adjust the ambient, diffuse and specular colors of the material, as well as a shininess parameter, in order to enhance the reading of the characters of the inscription.

The 3-D file can also be lit from various directions. Its surface texture can be changed and its relief can even be exaggerated.

Minimum curvature texturing

This picture shows one of the possibilities, called minimum curvature texturing. Here the computer searches for the flattest curve that will pass through a given point on the surface. If the point is at the bottom of a depression — like a carved letter — then it has a negative value. The computer collates numbers for each point.

Then, to make the numbers visible, the negative values can be assigned a darker blue. So this is not at all like a normal photograph: it is a mapping of numerical values that record curvature.

Flattening the stone's surface

The natural fluctuations in the surface of the stone are then removed using IDL, Image Data Language. The idea is to substract the background height fluctuations whose frequencies are below the frequency of the inscription in order to make it appear as if it had been written on a flat surface.

This is the original 3-D model, imported into IDL and shown as a "height field" — like a topographic map. The 'haze' color table in IDL makes the highest parts gold and the lowest purple.

There is a low-frequency variation in height across the model (a shallow dip, top to bottom, like a valley) that impedes a clear reading of the inscription. In order to remove it the image is processed using "wavelet filtering,"; a result is shown in the photo below.

Movies from single photographs

It is also possible to make movies from the 3-D model. At the bottom of the page is a still image from a synthetic video sequence generated by importing the 3D model into the 3D Studio Max software. An artificial texture with high reflectance properties is applied to the model and different light conditions were simulated by moving a projector in circle around the model. (The only other technology that allows films to be made from single photos is holography.)

What does the inscription say?

The 3-D file (for example at left) compares favorably with an old photograph (next page).

Even so, the inscription on the monument is almost completely illegible, because lichen and water damage obscure it. Reading is also problematic because of the possibility that the inscriber used a "deluxe" uncial script. This is most clear in lines 2 and 5 (see the diagram on page 219). Examples similar to the script used in the highly decorated gospel incipits in both the Book of Lindisfarne and the Book of Kells (see Chapter 15) suggest that the inscription would be difficult to decipher even if it was completely legible.

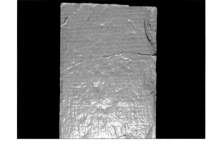

The layout on the stone also makes interpretation difficult. The carver set out parallel lines as a boundary or marker for the lettering and at times it is difficult to decipher when a letter begins and where the ruled line ends. A clear example of this is the lozenge shaped O. In the text given below, it is therefore sometimes shown as bracketed, and sometimes not, reflecting this difficulty.

Line 1	OP … M..A..O I
Line 2	AV …X I O Z I …III
Line 3	..O.....................OOI
Line 4	D..I........................
Line 5	BIOIRII..AINOIM LAI
Line 6	Dern(ad) O(ε)G I D

Here letters within parentheses indicate a possible reading and ellipses (…) indicate illegible parts of the inscription.

Scanning the world's sculpture

Scans of sculpture have been initiated in several countries. The National Technical University in Athens has scanned a model of Praxiteles's *Hermes* at a theoretical resolution of 0.17mm. In 1998, Stanford University launched the "Digital Michelangelo" project, which digitized Michelangelo's *David* at a theoretical resolution of 0.27mm. (In fact, the model is at 1mm resolution, partly because of the large dataset; the theoretical resolution is limited by the marble Michelangelo used, which is slightly translucent and grainy.)

Is a sculpture or a monument well enough preserved at 1mm resolution? Certainly that is finer than any verbal description, and finer than anything required by historical and critical analyses.

The copy becomes the original

The 3-D digital archives that are being built up are unprecedented in art history and archeologg. For the first time, the copy not only replaces but surpasses the original object: and it does so by being digital rather than analog — by consisting of discrete data points rather than a continuum of marble, stone, or plaster. Eventually, with degradation or loss of the original, the 3-D scan might become the new original.

Allegories of reading

The Irish project has also uncovered a lovely example of reading that is not quite reading. In Lismore Cathedral, in County Waterford, Ireland, there is a relief sculpture showing a man with an open book. The book is illegible, but when it is laser scanned, letters appear.

And yet… it isn't quite legible. The figure is in the style known as Hiberno-Romanesque, from 1150-1190, but the book he was meant to show us cannot quite be read. Like many of the scans made by the inscribed stones project, it results in a dramatic increase in visibility that does not quite lead to an increase in legibility. Sometimes visual images are rich with *apparent* meaning, and still poor in articulable meaning.

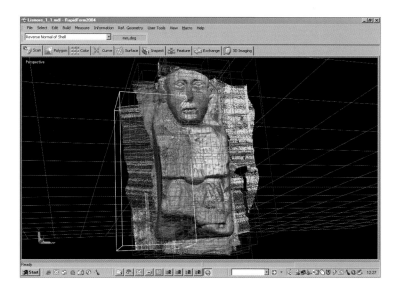

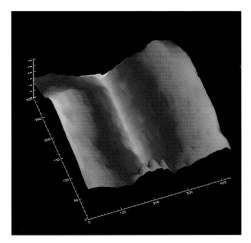

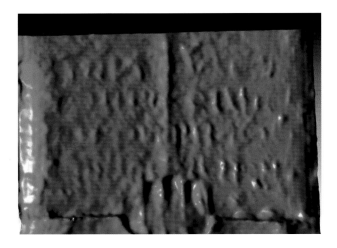

For further reading

An essay "Laser Profilometry of Medieval Inscribed Stones," including the stone described here, is at: www.foundationsirishculture.ie/main.php?id=4; and see also graphics.lcs.mit.edu/~dorsey/papers/stone/. For more on scanning stones, see: Julie Dorsey, Alan Edelman, et al., "Modelling and Rendering of Weathered Stone," *Computer Graphics* (Proceedings Annual Conference 1999, ACM SIGGRAPH) 3 (2004); and Alistair Carty, "Digital Recording of Pictish Sculpture," *Archaeoptics* 4 (2004), at www.archaeoptics.co.uk. Technical information is given in Maria Tsakiri, Charalambos Ioannidis, and Alistair Carty, "Laser Scanning Issues for the Geometrical Recording of a Complex Statue," www.archaeoptics.co.uk. For other cases, see "The Stonehenge Lasershow," *British Archaeology* 73 (November 2003); www.britarch.ac.uk/ba/ba73/feat1.shtml; www.stonehengelaserscan.org; and For the Digital Michelangelo Project see graphics.stanford.edu/data/mich/.

23

Deformation of Grains in Sandstone Rock

Pat Meere and Kieran Mulchrone

Microscopic grains in sandstones are slowly deformed by tectonic forces within the rock. A study by Pat Meere, a geologist, Kieran Mulchrone, a mathematician, and Kingshuk Roy Choudhury, a statistician, uses a combination of grain measurements from actual rocks along with mathematical models of how ideal grains deform, in order to statistically quantify the amount of strain associated with the deformation event. (Strain includes translation, distortion, rotation, and dilation — all the things that can happen to grains in rocks.)

The thin sections

They begin with samples of a continental and marine sandstone, cut in thin sections and observed under a polarizing microscope. The view in the opening photo is 2 mm across.

(The colors in one part of the photo are produced by the polarizing microscope; such colors contain information about the crystal orientations of the grains.)

An undeformed sample

The photo shows what is known as a *low strain regime:* that is, the grains are not strongly deformed. This image shows quartz grains (Q), in random orientations. Also present is a grain of siltstone (L), and large piece of mica (M), which shows the polarisation colors.

A deformed sample.

In the sample shown at the top of page 227, the grains have been deformed by pressure; the grains are clearly both distorted and aligned. The object of this experiment is to model such changes.

Outlining grains

Using customized image-analysis software developed by Kingshuk Roy Choudhury, Meere and Mulchrone defined the boundaries of selected quartz grains, called *clasts*. (Notice the red outlines in the photo on the lower-left on the next page).

It would be possible to define these outlines manually, but automated methods are preferable because they make use of multiple images, each made with a different orientation of polarized light, resulting in interpolated outlines that are more accurate than outlines drawn by hand.

The shape factor

Each grain has a *shape factor,* which is determined by matching it to an ellipse (see the top illustration on page 228). This is similar to the determination of the shape factor discussed in Chapter 3. What matters here is the *aspect ratio* of each ellipse (the ratio of its long and short axes) and its *orientation* — those data are then used to estimate strain.

The mathematical model

Next comes the mathematical modeling of the deformations that are observed in the samples. Mulchrone uses the physics of fluids to derive equations describing the deformation of individual grains. In this model grains can be more or less viscous than the surrounding material (i.e. harder or softer). In two dimensions a grain (with long axis a and short axis b, whose long axis makes an angle $\varnothing$ with the x-axis) changes shape and orientation according to the following equations:

$$\frac{d\varnothing}{dt} = ?\,(L_{21} - L_{12}) +$$

$$\frac{(a + b)\,(a^2 + b^2 + 2ab\,(\mu_r - 1))\,((\,L_{12} + L_{21})\,\cos2\varnothing - 2L_{11}\,\sin2\varnothing)}{2\,(a - b)\,(a^2 + b^2 + 2ab\mu_r)}$$

$$\frac{da}{dt} = \frac{a\,(a + b)^2\,\mu_r\,(2L_{11}\,\cos2\varnothing + (L_{12} + L_{21})\,\sin2\varnothing}{2((a^2 + b^2)\,\mu_r + 2ab)}$$

$$\frac{db}{dt} = \frac{a\,(a + b)^2\,\mu_r\,(2L_{11}\,\cos2\varnothing + (L_{12} + L_{21})\,\sin2\varnothing}{2((a^2 + b^2)\,\mu_r + 2ab)}$$

where all the L's describe the external flow and μ_r is the ratio of the external to the internal viscosities. These equations are highly non-linear and reflect the complexity of the motions.

Mathematical graphics

The bottom illustration on the next page is a screen snapshot from animation software developed to visualize the mathematical model. In the top-left frame, a

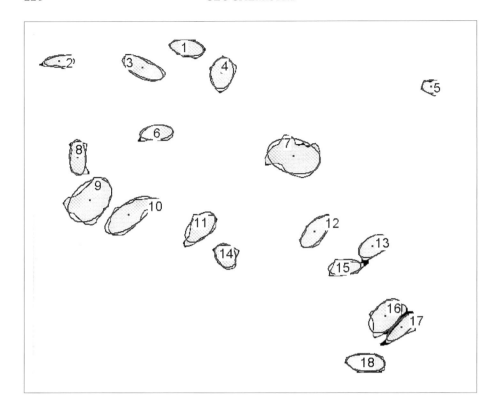

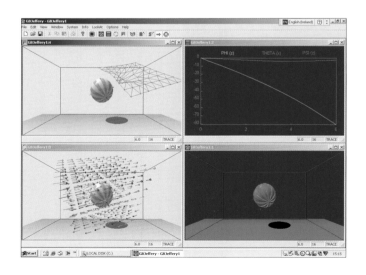

triangular grid of points displays how the surrounding material deforms due to the motion of a nearby grain, which is modelled as a rigid ellipsoid.

In the bottom-left frame the arrows show the velocity of surrounding material near a rigid ellipsoid. The top-right frame gives a conventional 2D graph of the variation of ellipsoid angles against time; and the bottom-right image gives an uncluttered view of the ellipsoid as it moves with time.

Combining observation and calculation

The project involves both observation and calculation: observation of large numbers of grains in thin sections, and mathematical models of grains. The results can be compared statistically.

As with all scientific work, it is necessary to continuously question the methods and assumptions; the research is ongoing. Meere and Mulchrone hope to improve their methodological approach and gain a better understanding of the physics involved in grain deformation, thereby enabling the construction of more realistic mathematical models.

The place of images

Note, then, the very complex role images play: they provide the raw data, but they are analyzed by an automated image-analysis routine. Images serve as helpful aids in Mulchrone's mathematical modeling, but the end result in both Meere's analyses and Mulchrone's models is mathematical data, which are then compared statistically — that is, independently of vision.

For further reading

Pat Meere and Kieran Mulchrone, "The Effect of Sample Size On Geological Strain Estimation From Passively Deformed Clastic Sedimentary Rocks," *Journal of Structural Geology* 25 (2003): 1587-95; Kieran Mulchrone, F. O'Sullivan, and Pat Meere, "Finite Strain Estimation Using The Mean Radial Length of Elliptical Objects With Bootstrap Confidence Intervals," *Journal of Structural Geology* 25 (2003): 529-39; Kieran Mulchrone and K. Roy Choudhury, "Fitting An Ellipse To An Arbitrary Shape: Implications For Strain Analysis," *Journal of Structural Geology* 26 (2004): 143-53.

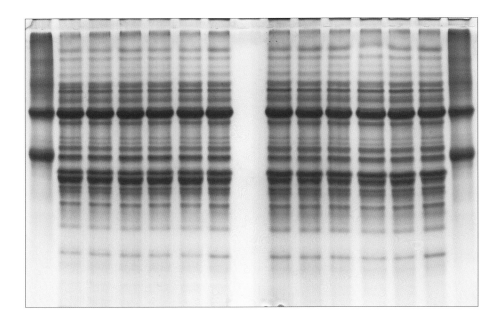

24

Gel Electrophoresis of Cheddar Cheese
Paul McSweeney

These pictures are from a study of the caseins in Cheddar cheese; casein is the principal protein of milk, and the structural matrix of cheese.

Most cheese varieties are ripened for periods ranging from about two weeks to two or more years. During ripening, microbiological and biochemical changes occur which result in the development of the flavour and texture characteristic of the variety.

Electrophoresis is a technique used in biochemistry and food science to separate and identify proteins. (The image itself is called an electrophoretogram.) In the opening photo, the column on the left is casein. The next six lanes are six samples of cheese, each two months old. Then come six lanes of cheeses that are six months old, and finally another reference lane of casein. It's apparent that the caseins change during the aging of the cheese, fragmenting into separate chemicals.

The process

Droplets of cheese (dissolved in a buffer) are placed at the top of the gel, and an electric field is applied. In the photos on the next two pages, the gel is attached to the source of electric current.

Depending on the pH of their environment, proteins may be positively or negatively charged. Thus, they can move in an electric field and are attracted down the lane towards the oppositely charged electrode. The proteins are differently charged, and move at different rates; each short horizontal band is therefore one type of protein — either one of the caseins or one of the products produced from them by the action of the enzymes chymosin (used to coagulate the milk) or plasmin (a chemical naturally present in milk).

After the proteins have been given a chance to move along the channels, the electricity is turned off, and a dye is used to reveal them. (Otherwise they would be invisible.)

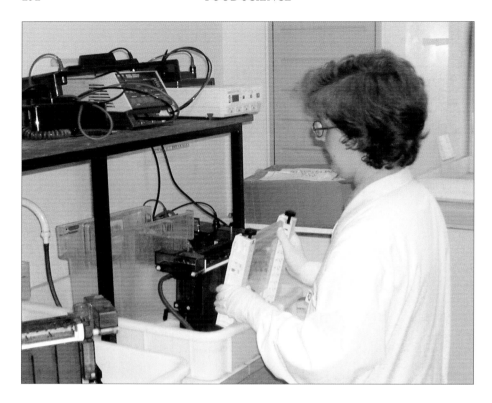

Visual analysis

This gel shows electrophoretograms of whole casein, distinguished into α_s1- and β-casein (see the diagram on page 235). They are degraded during ripening. In the two month-old Cheddar cheese samples, β-casein has been degraded slightly by the action of plasmin, an enzyme indigenous to milk, to form three peptides.

The α_s1-Casein has been degraded almost completely to two peptides, α_s1-CN and α_s1-CN. The agent that effected the degrading is chymosin, the enzyme in rennet used to coagulate the milk.

The numbers in parentheses denote the fragments of the protein cut off by the enzyme. Thus "f29-209" is a portion of β-casein. The whole molecule of β-casein is 209 amino acids long; "f29-209" is a fragment cut along the peptide bond between amino acids at positions 28 and 29.

The uselessness of the visual evidence

What can be seen on the original photo? A trained eye would see right away that the intensities of certain bands on the left half aren't the same as the intensites of

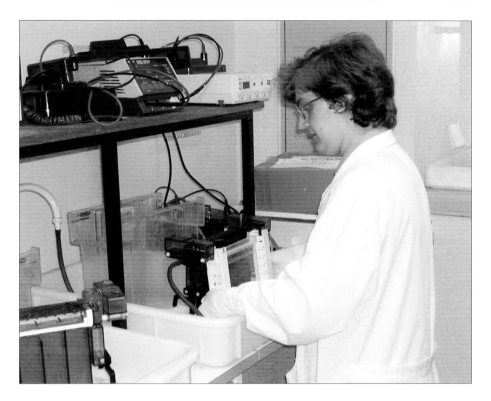

bands on the right half. For example compare the bands labelled α_s1-CN (f102-199): they are denser on the right, in the cheeses that have been aged longer — indicating more of the casein has been degraded into that particular fragment. Clearly, however, it is not easy to make these distinctions by eye, and normally researchers do not use images like the first one, or even like the one that has been labelled.

Statistical analysis

Instead the electrophoretograms are recorded by scanning the gel, and the amounts of each protein are quantified by densitometry. In the picture below, from another study, the lanes are placed horizontally underneath scans which quantify the density of each protein band.

Data like this can then be analyzed statistically, across a number of samples, by multivariate analysis. Visual evidence is not important. Despite the lovely blue-and-white picture, what is available to the eye is only a way-station to quantifiable information. This result is disappointing for an analysis bent on

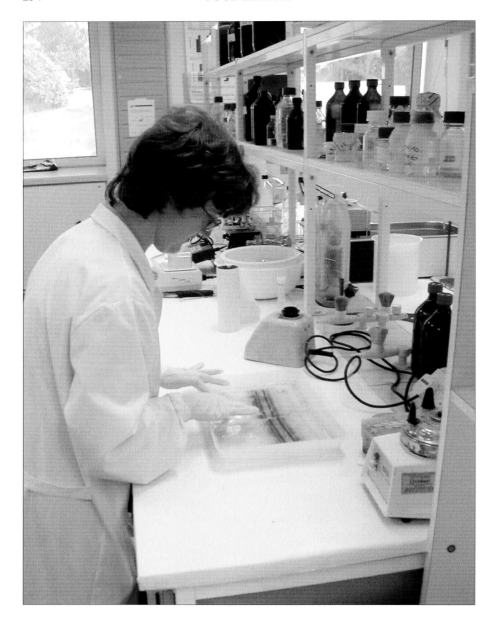

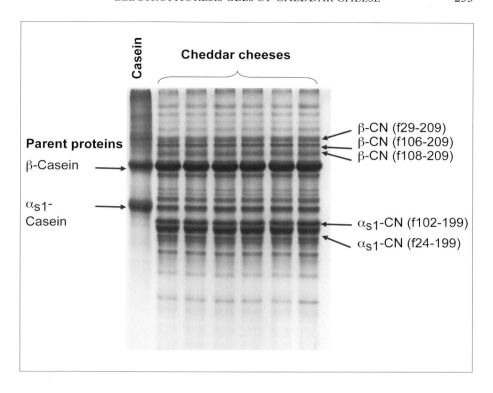

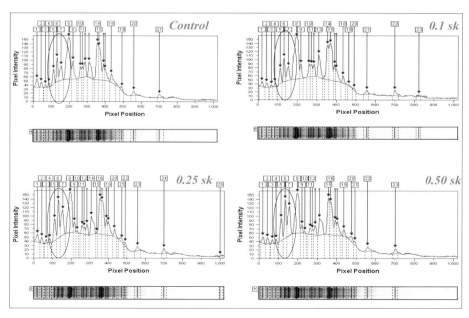

visualization, but it is broadly typical of the sciences, where the visual is likely to be a starting point that can sooner or later be discarded.

For further reading:

McSweeney, "Biochemistry of Cheese Ripening: Introduction and Overview," in *Cheese: Chemistry, Physics and Microbiology*, vol. 1, *General Aspects*, 3rd edition, edited by P.F. Fox, P.L.H. McSweeney, T.M. Cogan and T.P. Guinee (London: Elsevier, 2004); Upadhyay, V.K., P.L.H. McSweeney, A.A.A. Magboul and P.F. Fox, "Proteolysis in Cheese During Ripening," in ibid; and McSweeney, "Biochemistry of Cheese Ripening," *International Journal of Dairy Technology* 57 no. 2/3 (2004): 127-44.

25

Europhlukes

Emer Rogan and Simon Ingram

In Günther Grass's novel *Dog Years,* there is a boy whose eyes are so sharp he can tell every blackbird in a flock. Ornithologists might love to have that ability. Primatologists like Jane Goodall develop the ability to tell every individual in a group of apes or monkeys. But in general, naturalists have to be content with counting bodies, and they are often unsure exactly which individual is which.

Europhlukes is an attempt to remedy that for the study of dolphins and whales. The project begins with a database of photographs of the fins of whales and dolphins. Typically the fins have scars and scratches — bites from predators, or just the wear and tear of normal life. Those marks serve as fingerprints.

Examples

Five examples are given here. In bottlenose dolphins the most useful identifying feature is the dorsal fin; in sperm whales the trailing edge of the tail flukes are the most uniquely marked feature.

Long-term study

By repeatedly photographing and identifying uniquely marked individuals scientists can follow these animals between years and between geographic areas. In this way it is possible to examine an individual's ranging patterns, its social behaviour and other aspects of its ecology.

Automated recognition of individuals

Just as in the police software that identifies people from surveillance cameras, Europhlukes is developing the capacity to instantly identify individual whales and dolphins.

Europhlukes is EU funded, and is coordinating whale and dolphin researchers working throughout Atlantic Europe. The project is establishing a shared on-line data base of photos and related data to assist in the data storage and matching process.

Computer identification

In the two screenshots, the yellow line created by the computer shows the unique edge shapes of whales' tails and dolphins' dorsal fins.

The future of computer-assisted identification

Computers analyzing CCTV camera feeds can already identify people in crowds. (The crucial parameter in those identifications is the distance between the eyes.

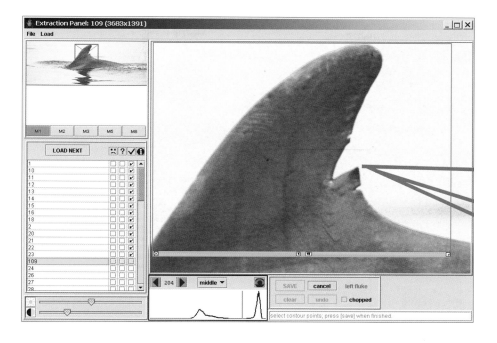

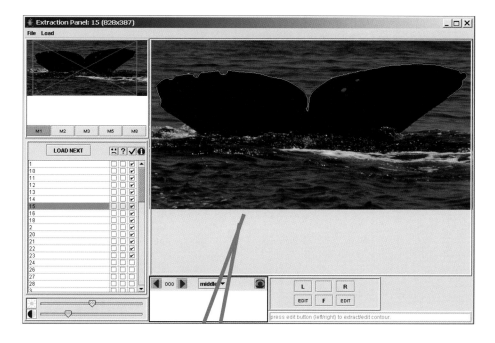

Wrap-around dark glasses can help foil the cameras.) Anonymity in crowds is, in theory, a thing of the past.

With projects like Europhlukes, it may be only a matter of time before all animals are individuals — and there are no more flocks, or pods, or herds, but only individual animals with numbers (or names).

For further reading

Visit http://europhlukes.maris2.nl/.

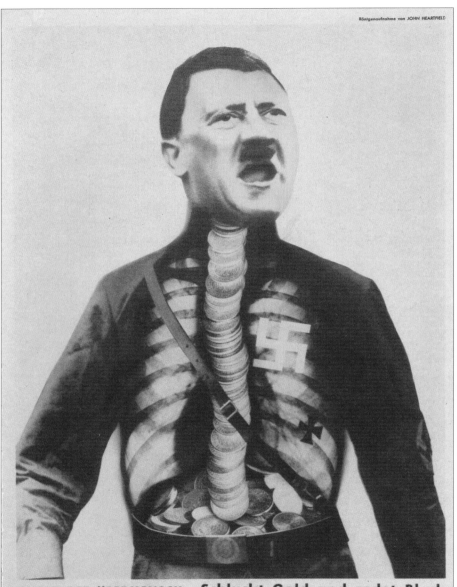

ADOLF, DER ÜBERMENSCH: **Schluckt Gold und redet Blech**

675

26

Sabine Kriebel

Using Photography as a Weapon

Most images in this book have no immediately apparent political meaning. By comparison, many images studied in the history of art have overt religious, ethical, and political significance.

The related field of visual studies is concerned with images in mass communication — many of which have political purposes. From a visual-studies standpoint, *all* the images in this book have their politics, even if it goes unremarked.

Visual studies sets out to use images — *any* images — as occasions to educate students as reflective members of society. Visual studies is therefore opportunistic: it can take images from any field and read them with an eye to the political work they do.

This chapter gives a brief sample of the analysis of the politics of images.

John Heartfield

John Heartfield was the pseudonym adopted by the German artist Helmut Herzfelde to protest German chauvinism and anti-British sentiment during World War I; he openly took sides with the enemy during period of virulent nationalism.

Anglicizing his name signaled Heartfield's internationalist convictions, as much as it declared his Dadaist predilections. His involvement with Berlin Dada was a leftist, anti-militarist, anti-bourgeois protest in which he developed the medium of photomontage as an anarchist weapon. During the 1920s and 1930s, he became the image-maker of the German Communist Left, producing a copious supply of mass-reproduced posters, book jackets, and satirical photomontages. Most significantly, he made 237 photomontages for the popular left-wing *Arbeiter Illustrierte Zeitung (AIZ)*, or *Workers Illustrated Magazine* from 1929-1938. As a result he was regularly persecuted by the National Socialist regime, spied on by Gestapo agents, and twice forced into exile because of his provocative pictures.

Seizing viewers' attentions

The goal of Heartfield's photomontages was to seize the passing gaze in a public sphere saturated by the photographic image. These photomontages sought not just to attract the eye, like a seductive consumer advertisement, but labored to stimulate political consciousness through aggressive visual means. They aimed to reveal the realities behind appearances, to take the supposedly incontrovertible "realness" of a photograph, and by cutting and reassembling photographic images and text, manipulate them to elucidate certain conditions not revealed by the original image.

The Meaning of the Hitler Salute — Millions Stand Behind Me!

The photomontage on the next page was published on the cover of *AIZ* on October 16, 1932, just two weeks before an election. It lays bare the "millions" that stand behind Adolf Hitler. Here we see capitalism, translated into corpulent excess punctuated by gleaming ring, handing a diminutive Hitler millions of Rentenmark. The small Führer hand flops back limply, rather than thrusts dynamically forward, to nonchalantly receive those millions of support.

Adolf the Übermensch

Heartfield's *"Adolf the Übermensch: Swallows Gold and Spouts Junk"* of July 17, 1932 (the opening image in this chapter) "sees through" Hitler's persuasive speeches using a technological device more potent than the photographic lens, penetrating surfaces where cameras can only record them. Through an X-Ray photograph of Hitler's insides, we discover that Hitler's entire gastrointestinal tract is clogged with coins.

Like photomontage, the X-Ray is a visual device that intervenes in the surfaces of reality in order to lay bare "true" conditions. The montage was plastered all over Berlin in anticipation for the July Reichstag elections and provoked fistfights between Nazis and Communists.

Deutschland Deutschland über Alles!

While John Heartfield gained prominence for his radical leftist photomontage, he was also greatly admired by the commercial sector, particularly for his election posters and book jacket covers.

His photomontages for the satirical book *Deutschland Deutschland über Alles!*, a text-image collaboration with the well-known author Kurt Tucholsky, was widely acclaimed and also became the focus of public controversy in 1929.

The framed print

By contrast, Heartfield's 1924 dust jacket for the collected stories of the best-
selling American author Jack London is more conservative in its design and
content. The montage juxtaposes a photographic portrait of Jack London, a com-

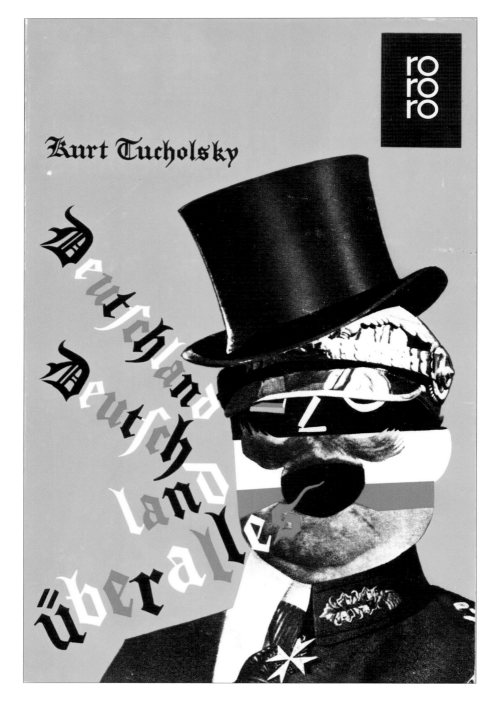

mitted socialist, with visual fragments associated with his stories of high adventure and survival. The cover montage not only reveals the book's assembled contents in a single glance but also reinforces London's leftist message of resolute and heroic struggle against a hostile environment.

Photomontage as a medium

More economical than film, more pervasive in daily life than the cinema, photomontage in the 1920s and 1930s became a political weapon, a form through which to shape mass-consciousness before radio and television were competitive forms of everyday information.

For further reading

Dawn Ades, *Photomontage* (London: Thames and Hudson, 1976); David Evans and Sylvia Gohl, *Photomontage: A Political Weapon* (London: Gordon Fraser, 1986); David Evans, *John Heartfield, AIZ-VI, 1930-1938* (New York: Kent Fine Art, 1991); and Peter Pachnicke, *John Heartfield* (New York: Harry Abrams, 1992).

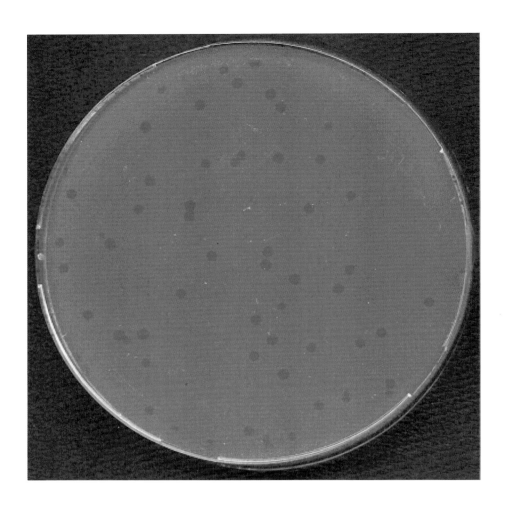

27

Visualising Viruses
Stephen McGrath

The biologist Stephen Harrison wrote a book called *What Does a Virus Look Like?*. In it he considered over ten different kinds of images of viruses, made with different instruments. They are not all compatible — they cannot be assembled into one perfect picture. Harrison concluded that viruses don't "look like" anything except the sum total of those images.

William Wimsatt, a philosopher of science, has called this problem the "thicket of illustration": no one strategy will do, he notes, when it comes to picturing things as complex as DNA. Here we consider five different ways of producing images of viruses.

The plaque assay

Phages are obligate parasites of bacterial cells. They have no intrinsic metabolism and are totally inert in the absence of their bacterial hosts. They attach to the bacterial cells in a tail-first orientation, triggering the release of the DNA from the phage head, where it has been held under immense pressure.

The *plaque assay* is a method used in the laboratory to visualize the bacteriophage life cycle. An agar plate is seeded with a "lawn" of bacteria that has been mixed with some phages (see opening illustration). The clear spots on the plate show where a phage has infected a bacterial cell and the progeny phages have killed the cells around it, causing a clear zone or "plaque."

At this stage, no special optical equipment is necessary to locate the phages.

Transmission electron microscopy

The main structural features of phages can be seen in the large TEM image, below. This is the lactococcal bacteriophage Tuc2009. Toward the top is the head, containing the DNA; then the tail; and at the bottom the structure that recognizes the host cells and contains the adsorption apparatus.

TEMs work on the analogy of light microscopes, but they shine a beam of electrons through the specimen (another example is in Chapter 21, page 212). Whatever part is transmitted is projected onto a phosphor screen for the user to see. This is a typical, full-resolution TEM image; the original is 1280 x 1024 pixels in 16-bit grayscale — these images do not need to have ultrahigh resolution.

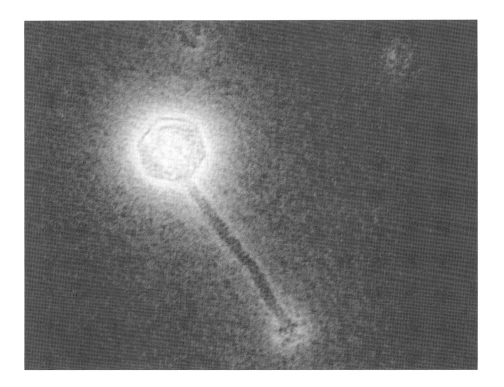

Gene mapping

The first step in gene mapping is sequencing. The familiar base pairs of DNA — the rungs in its ladder — are sequenced. The graph that results is called a chromatogram. The names of the base pairs can be read off the graph (in five print, below the horizontal baseline); the heights of the peaks show the confidence level of the analysis.

The graph reproduced below illustrates the genome of the bacteriophage Tuc2009. Its complete genome sequence has been determined and the individual genes contained within it identified using a set of criteria based on the recognition of patterns and signatures in the DNA sequence. Each of the arrows represents an individual gene. The arrows are arranged in three rows, just to make them more visible. At the top of the image is a map of the parts of the phage that are formed by the different genes.

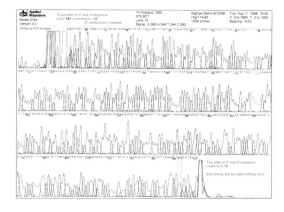

The colored arrows indicate genes coding for proteins to which physiological functions have been assigned. Red indicates that a function has been assigned on the basis of experimental work, whereas green denotes that a function has been assigned on the basis of the similarity

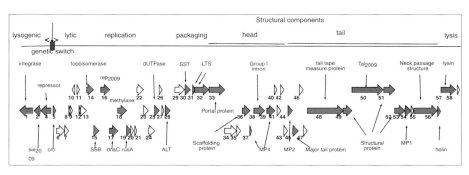

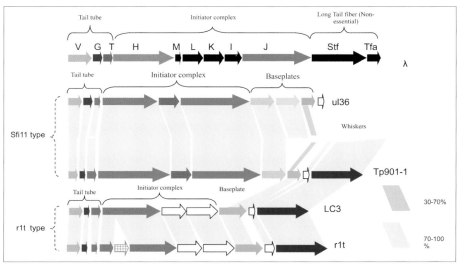

of that protein to experimentally verified proteins encoded by other phages. Computer analysis allows us to predict which proteins will form part of the bacteriophage structure, but the actual visualization of these proteins is the only definitive proof.

The gene sequence in the Tuc2009 can then be compared with genes in other bacteriophages (diagram at the bottom of the previous page). The genes occur in slightly different places, but they can sometimes be correlated, making it possible to determine some of their functions.

Electrophoresis

The electrophoresis technique is used to separate and visualise individual proteins in a biological sample. (Compare Chapter 24, showing gel electrophoresis of cheddar cheese.)

The protein bands in lane 1 (image on the next page) represent a standard mixture of proteins of known size to which test proteins are compared. Each of the bands in lane 2 represents individual proteins that constitute the bacteriophage. Single bands representing individual proteins may then be cut from the gel and further analyzed in order to determine the sequence of amino acids that they contain.

This type of analysis is dependent on the successful separation of the individual protein constituents into discrete homogenous bands as well as the presence of sufficient concentrations of proteins in these bands. The amino acid sequences may then be compared to those predicted from the gene map, thus allowing the identification of the structural proteins. You can compare the labeled protein bands in lane 2 to the arrows in the gene map (middle illustration on the previous page) to see the location of the genes that encode the proteins.

Immunogold electron microscopy

Data from the electrophoresis analysis reveals whether a particular protein forms part of the phage structure or not, but it doesn't locate the precise location of the protein on the bacteriophage. Antibodies that are highly specific for individual proteins may be generated using a variety of genetic and biochemical techniques. Labeling these antibodies with gold makes them appear as dense black spots when viewed under a transmission electron microscope. When the antibodies are mixed with the bacteriophage they specifically recognize and "tag" their cognate protein on the bacteriophage structure, thus marking the precise location of the protein.

The first panel is a TEM of the Tuc2009 bacteriophage without the addition of gold-labelled antibodies. Gold-labelled antibodies specifically recognizing individual proteins are added in the other pictures and are indicated on the panels. Their encoding genes are also included — the same numbers appear on the image just above (top of p. 255).

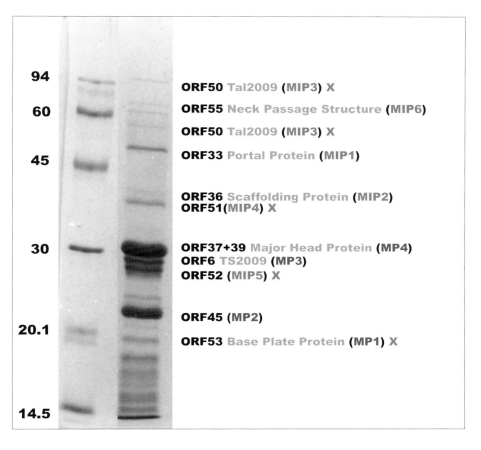

ORF50 Tal2009 (MIP3) X
ORF55 Neck Passage Structure (MIP6)
ORF50 Tal2009 (MIP3) X
ORF33 Portal Protein (MIP1)
ORF36 Scaffolding Protein (MIP2)
ORF51(MIP4) X
ORF37+39 Major Head Protein (MP4)
ORF6 TS2009 (MP3)
ORF52 (MIP5) X
ORF45 (MP2)
ORF53 Base Plate Protein (MP1) X

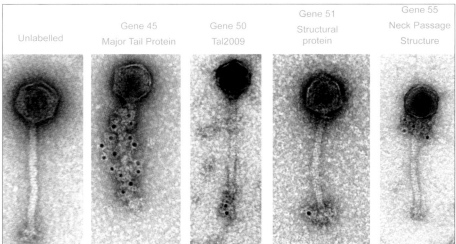

Unlabelled | Gene 45 Major Tail Protein | Gene 50 Tal2009 | Gene 51 Structural protein | Gene 55 Neck Passage Structure

The process of generating these antibodies can be laborious and expensive, and the success of the tagging of the specific protein on the phage is dependent on a number of critical factors such as the quality of the antibody and the accessibility of the protein on the phage structure to the antibody.

Other kinds of pictures

In addition to these kinds of images, virologists also make extremely detailed images of all the atoms in parts of the bacteriophages (image at the bottom of this page). At the other end of the scale of detail, virologists find it useful to make schematic pictures of the different parts of the virus, to model how they might be put together (image at the top of the next page). Ideally, each part corresponds to a known gene (image at the bottom of the next page).

Conclusions

These are just eight of the ten or more methods of visualizing viruses. Clearly, no single representational method is sufficient. The opposite of the "thicket" of representation is the assumption, common in fine art, that a single image — say, the *Mona Lisa* — is not only sufficient but definitional for its subject. No further representations can even be imagined, except pastiches. In this case, however, the object does not exist except as a series of partly incommensurate representations.

For further reading

More on the visualization of viruses: Stephen Harrison, "What Do Viruses Look Like?" *The Harvey Lectures* 85 (1991); James Elkins, *The Domain of Images* (Ithaca NY: Cornelll University Press, 1999), chapter 3.

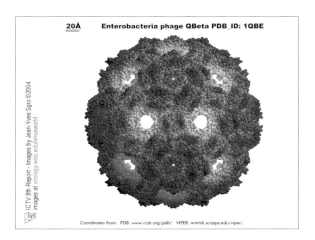

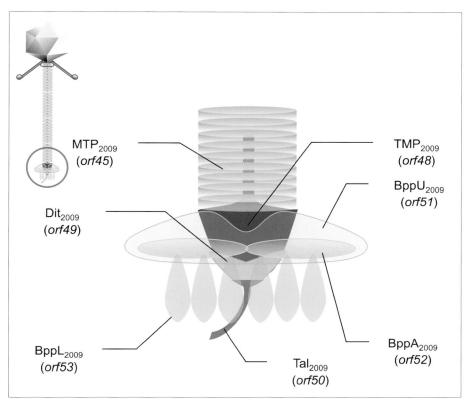

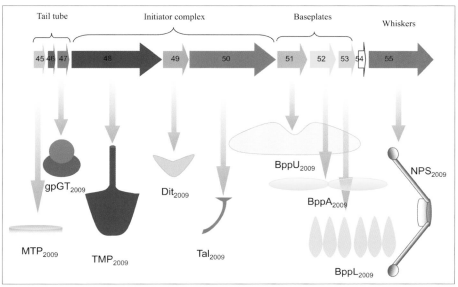

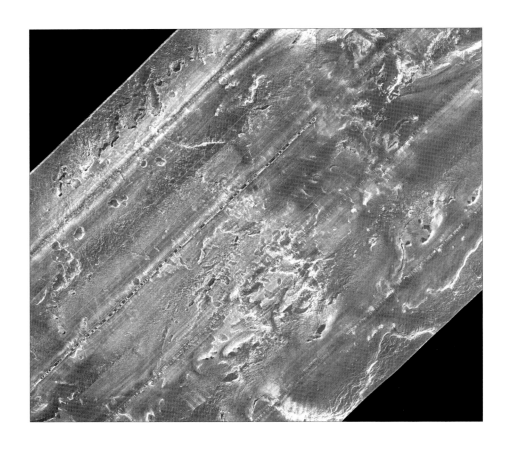

28

Imaging the Seabed using Side-Scan Sonar

Andy Wheeler

To image the sea floor, it is necessary to translate one kind of sensing — hearing sound echoes off the seabed — into another kind — ordinary greyscale images. Like all translations, this one produces "false friends": forms that look familiar, but are not.

How the image was taken

The side-scan sonar system used to acquire the image is called TOBI. TOBI weights 1.8 tons; it was towed 300 meters above the seabed, several kilometers behind the vessel. TOBI emits a ping and then listens for the return echo on two transceivers (port and starboard).

Side-scan sonar

The side-scan sonar produces raw data that can be plotted at sea in real-time. After the side-scan sonar emits a ping, the transceivers initially record silence as the sound wave travels through the water column. This is followed by the first echo from the seabed directly below sonar where it is the nearest. The echo continues, ending with the last return from the seabed furthest away on the extreme port or starboard. The

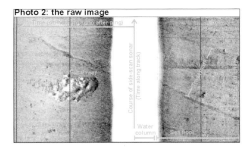

Photo 2: the raw image

time delay in hearing the echoes, measured in milliseconds, can be translated into distance from port or starboard. In this way the sonar beam scans the seabed. When the echo is fully recorded, a new ping is emitted and another echo is recorded — by that time the apparatus has moved forward so it images the next piece of the seafloor. By plotting the echoes against time in grayscale, one next to the other, a preliminary image of the seafloor is obtained.

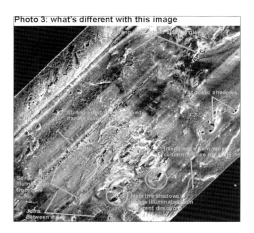

Photo 3: what's different with this image

In the photo above, the starboard image is on the right, and the port on the left. The ship travels over the seabed as shown. A gap, directly below the ship, is marked "water column." Two features of the seafloor are marked: a coral reef, and grooves left by trawling.

What different about this image

It is tempting to look at the finished image as if it is a black and white photograph of the seabed. In fact, it is a black and white *sonograph* of the seabed that has been made from a number of strip images.

It's possible to list the features that can be misleading:

First, there is the series of diagonal lines across the image following the path of the sonar. (They do not indicate features of the seafloor.)

Second, there are fainter lines where the strips join. (Marked at the bottom of photo)

Third, there are shadows, but they do not behave in a familiar fashion.

Sonar shadows

Each strip is illuminated from the center (from the sonar path) out to the edge so that acoustic shadows (like normal shadows) fall to the left and right of this line. When the strips are put together, the new image is illuminated by sound in a very unusual way: from the center of each strip rather than from one direction only.

More oddities

Fourth — continuing the list of things that aren't "normal" about this image — the interpretation of bright and dark areas also differs from how we would see a black and white photo. Dark areas are formed from seabed that returns weak echoes and bright areas from seabed that gives back strong echoes.

In a similar way to photographs, this is partly

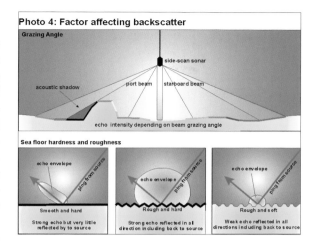

Photo 4: Factor affecting backscatter

caused by slope angle (grazing angle): steep slopes facing the sonar path are bright (like sunlight slopes) and slopes facing away are dark. However, strong echoes (bright values) can also be formed by hard or rough seabed, which reflects more sound.

The bottom of this diagram shows even more complexities of hardness and roughness. The image at the bottom of the previous page shows a couple of the permutations (middle and top). This does not correspond well with ordinary objects illuminated by light: this image has to be *learned* before it can be seen.

And one last oddity

Fifth, an illusion is formed when sound is bent (or diffracted) by density differences in the water column producing a series of wavy lines due to echo return clustering. This is apparent at the edge of imaged strips where the echo has had to travel the furthest. It is marked on the lower right of the labeled photo at the bottom of the previous page.

How the image is assembled and cleaned up

To produce the final image, the raw data from the side-scan sonar needs to be processed. First, the port and starboard images are stitched together by removing the silent "water column." This has been done large image.

Next, across-track time has to be converted to across-track distance based on the speed of sound through water. Then, along-track time has to be converted to along-track distance based on the tow speed of the sonar and the ping-rate.

The image then has to be "navigated" — its global position fixed — based on ship's position (as determined by satellite) and the distance of the sonar behind the vessel. The overlaps between the outer edges of adjoining strips are neatly cut together. The entire image can then be enhanced to maximize density contrasts.

What is the topography?

When the image is complete, the trained eye can start to interpret the seabed features. There are two main difficulties with interpretation.

First, the image contains no topography so it can be difficult to tell if a change in grayscale is due to a change in slope, a change in seabed type, or both. This can be overcome by draping the image over a topographic reconstruction of the seabed obtained by depth soundings using different acoustic techniques. In the image at the bottom of this page, submarine canyons not obvious on the side-scan sonar become clearly visible. (Notice the canyons in this overlay, and compare them with the same features on the large image.)

Second and more fundamentally, the image is still only a grayscale image, reflecting differences in the intensity of the echo. In theory the same echo intensity can be generated by a soft but rough bottom and a hard but smooth bottom. The geologist makes a contextual interpretation, but that is only an experienced guess until it is confirmed (or "ground-truthed") by the collection of physical seabed samples or seabed photographs.

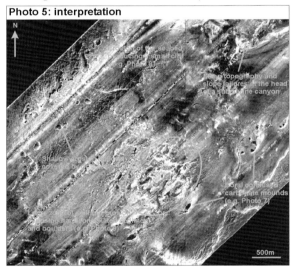

Photo 5: interpretation

The purpose of the study

This seabed mapping was undertaken to make the remote accessible. The sonar image provides a map that can be used by others to explore the seabed. The image has the advantage of not only showing seabed features but also the nature of the seabed sediment; that information is impor-

Photo 7: Irish coral reef with crinoids and fish

945m water depth · c.10cm

Photo 8: coral colonised top of submarine cliff

676m water depth · c.10cm

Photo 9: typical seabed showing exposure of boulder due to seabed erosion with coral

681m water depth · c.20cm

tant to fishermen trawling the seabed, marine mineral prospecting companies including oil companies, submarine cable layers and engineers who need to install seabed structures. Side-scan sonar can also be used to hunt for shipwrecks and salvage or check submarine dump sites.

The reason the university made this particular image was to understand what was happening in a particularly harsh environment where we suspected deep-water corals thrived. Following the creation of the image, a follow-up survey was undertaken "ground-truthing" interesting areas with sediment samples and video cameras mounded on a robotic submersible. Those images, shown with their original exhibition captions on the previous page, proved and refined our geological interpretations.

For instance, the bottom photo shows a boulder-strewn seabed. The boulders are too small to be seen by the side-scan sonar but they account for the strong return signal observed in that area. Without the video imagery we could only have said that there was a hard seabed there — possibly a rock platform, boulders, or something else.

Conclusion

There are two lessons here for the uses of the visual. First, as we have seen in Chapters 6,10 and 16, an image that appears to be an ordinary picture may not be. In this case, it may be necessary to elaborately re-train the eye to interpret such fundamental things as light and shade. Second, although the side-scan sonar allows us to map large areas and extract useful information it takes experience to read the results. The proof — "ground-truthing" — is a relatively simple photograph, video, or sediment sample. Mapping, here, precedes seeing.

For further reading

See first the website: www.marine-group.com/SonarPrimer/SideScanSonar.htm; then Andre M. Akhmetzhanov, Neil H. Kenyon, Micheal K. Ivanov, Andy Wheeler, Pavel V. Shashkin, and Tjeerd C.E. van Weering, "Giant Carbonate Mounds and Current Swept Seafloors on the Slopes of the Southern Rockall Trough," in *European Margin Sediment Dynamics: Side-scan Sonar and Seismic Images,* edited by Jurgen Mienert and Phil Weaver (Berlin: Springer Verlag, 2003), 203-210; Doug G. Masson, Brian J. Bett, Dave S.M. Billett, Colin L. Jacobs, Andy J. Wheeler and Russel B. Wynn, "The Origin of Deep-Water, Coral-Topped Mounds in the Northern Rockall Trough, Northeast Atlantic," *Marine Geology* 192 (2003): 215-37; Andy Wheeler, Maxim Kozachenko, Andres Beyer, Anneleen Foubert, Veerle A.I. Huvenne, Michael Klages, Doug G. Masson, Karine Olu-Le Roy and Jorn Thiede, "Sedimentary Processes and Carbonate Mounds in the Belgica Mound Province, Porcupine Seabight, NE Atlantic," in *Deep-Water Corals and Ecosystems,* edited by Andre Freiwald and J.Murray Roberts (Berlin: Springer Verlag, 2005), 571-603.

СТОЛПЪ И УТВЕРЖДЕНІЕ ИСТИНЫ.

FINIS AMORIS, UT DUO UNUM FIANT.
ПРЕДѢЛЪ ЛЮБВИ—ДА ДВОЕ ЕДИНО БУДУТЪ.

29

Metaphors of Light and Dark in Arabic and Russian Philosophy

Anna Zenkova

Philosophy is shot through with optical metaphors. Hegel's use of optical metaphors is discussed in Borch-Jakobsen's book *Lacan: The Absolute Master.* In the book by Martin Jay *Downcast Eyes: The Denigration of Vision in Twentieth-Century French Thought* the role of vision and optical metaphors in western philosophy, particularly France, was investigated. I will consider just two examples out of the hundreds possible: Arabic Peripatetic philosophy and philosophy of Illumination, and Russian *fin-de-siècle* philosophy.

Pavel Florenskiy

The book illustrations here are of Florenskiy's *The Pillar and Ground of the Truth: An Essay in Orthodox Theodicy in Twelve Letters.* He designed the cover himself, including the fonts, and the book is self-published. The legend under the two angels, *Fenis amoris ut duo unum fiant* ("Love makes two into one") is intended to express his principal metaphysical claim: the assertion that all created coexist with each other. Consider these three key terms in his text:

Truth (истина, estina)
Darkness (темнотиа, temnota)
Clearness (ясность, yasnost')

СТОЛПЪ И УТВЕРЖДЕНІЕ
ИСТИНЫ

опытъ православной ѳеодицеи
въ двѣнадцати письмахъ

свящ. Павла Флоренскаго

ἡ δε γνῶσις ἀγάπη γίνεται.
Св. Григорій Нисскій.

МОСКВА
1914.

In Florenskiy's work, the true "act of seeing" opposes false distanced seeing. Florenskiy suggests the ontological aspects of idea and knowledge by using the example of the Russian word "truth" (истина, *estina*). He noted that the word descends from Latin verb *est* (истина: that which exists). The important factor of sense-building in Russian philosophy, he argued, is the difference "egoistic false seeing," that is "the darkness" (темнота, *temnota*) and "living true seeing," that is joint action in which subject and object flow together in "the clearness" (ясность, *yasnost'*). The egoistic concentration of self on itself leads to neuropathological conditions, namely a condition of "being in darkness" and being "separated from whole world."

Hence the opposition between "true seeing" and "false seeing" is more significant than the opposition "visible" and "invisible," or between "obvious" and "hidden". Florenskiy argues that the perception of objects takes place intuitively, and is a direct contemplation of living reality as it is in itself: it is "the act of inner union of perceiving person and perceivable object." The question about true seeing becomes a question about the true observer and his or her place in the world. The "true seeing" is a perceptible joining of subject and world in common action. To be is "to be revealed"; and "to reveal" is to find truth.

Prozrachnyj and prizrachnyj

Transparency (прозрачный, *prozrachnyj*)
Spectral (призрачный, *prizrachnyj*)

Another important conceptual difference between West European and Russian philosophy is between transparency and the spectral or mirroring function in epistemology. In Russian "transparency" (прозрачный, *prozrachnyj*) and "spectral" (призрачный, *prizrachnyj*) have similar pronunciation. According to Florenskiy transparency isn't just a requirement of cognition, it is the highest human value. This value is as unavoidable as our desire for being in the world. Because of the ontological orientation of nineteenth-century Idealist Russian philosophy the metaphor "transparency" was gradually transformed from "transparency of the environment in which the object is located" to "transparency of the object."

By means of transparency the eye is like the light: it can penetrate body of matter. But true insight begins when the object that is recognized is understood as transparent. Understanding the play of transparent surfaces is understanding the inner and outer aspects of the object.

The Peripatetics and The Ishraqiyun

As a second example, consider terms in Arabic Peripatetic philosophy and Philosophy of Illumination. I will use texts by two famous representatives of the two schools: the Arabic Peripatetic al-Farabi, who had the name "Second Teacher" (after Aristotle); and the founder of the Philosophy of Illumination (the *Ishraqiyun*) al-Suhrawardi, who developed the Peripatetics' ideas.

Zuhir and batin

visible *zahir*	ظاهر
invisible *batin*	باطن

Manifest or (*zahir*) and latent or invisible (*batin*) are meta-categories in Arabic philosophy. Relations of the visible and the invisible in Arabic philosophy of the 10th and 11th centuries correspond neither to the dichotomy of truth and falsehood (as in Russian philosophy) nor to the dualism of appearance and essence. The distinction of visible and invisible, *zahir* and *batin,* exists in discussions of latentness as opposed to manifestness (or visibility) in the causality of the earlier Mutakallimun (a school that includes Abu al-Hudhail al-'Allaf, al-Ash'ari, Mu'tamir and others). This question was studied in detail by representatives of Peripatetic philosophy, and the philosophy of light or illumination (the *ishraqiyun*). Here I will not consider the differences among the schools, but concentrate on what they have in common.

The ontological aspect of the relation between *zahir* and *batin* is investigated in the *Book of Gems (Kitab al-fusus* كتاب الفصوص). The author of this book, Al-Farabi (878-950), is considered to be the follower of Peripatetic philosophy. In the *Kitab al-fusus,* manifestness (called *zahur* ظهور) is understood as the explicitness of all consequences — that is, grades of being — of the First Cause. Without explicitness First Cause annot be in itself; it must remain invisible. It is impossible to say that one thing can manifest the First Cause in full measure. Its latentness consists of its invisibility *as* itself.

So manifestness as visibility and latentness as invisibility are impossible without one other and lead to one other. The perception of a thing is the movement from visible to invisible and not the other way around.

Light of lights	
Nur al-anvar	الانوارنور
Close light	
Nur al-akrab	الاقربنور
Victorious light	
Kahir	قاهر

Nur al-anvar, nur al-akrab, kahir

Metaphors of light and dark specific to Arabic philosophy can be found in texts by the founder of the Philosophy of Illumination al-Suhrawardi, most important of them is *The Wisdom of Illumination (Himkat al-ishraq* حكمت الاشراق). According to the doctrine of Philosophy of Illumination everything consists of lights and their shadows, which emanated from the absolute unity of the *light of lights* (*Nur al-anvar*). For the Neoplatonic chain of emanations of minds (or intellects or angels), al-Suhrawardi substituted with his own chain of emanations of lights coming from united the light of lights, which he took to be identical with the Absolute (*almotluk* المطلق). According to al-Suhrawardi the total number of links in this chain of emanations is much more than the ten traditional grades of Peripatetic thought, which are a traditional element of Peripatetic doctrine.

The first emanation of Great Light (*nur al-a'zam*) al-Suhrawardi calls Archangel Brahman or "close light" (*nur al-akrab*). Because there is no barrier between it and the Light of Lights, the radiance of the Great Light falls directly to the Light of Lights. As a result of this fall and radiance there arises a new victorious light (*kahir* رهاق) on which fall both the Great Light and the First Light that are above it.

On the third light falls the second light (twice), Great Light, First Light, and so on. The perception of a thing which appears, according to the Philosophy of Illumination, as "irradiation," is the perception of a particular light that is one of the potentially endless aspects of God (*Allah* الله) or Truth (*hakika* حقيقة).

Conclusions

It is interesting to note that there are many investigations devoted to the analysis of visual metaphors in West European philosophy, but that Arabic and Russian philosophic texts have never been analyzed from this standpoint. I think that analysis of the ways of conceptualizing visual metaphors in different philosophical traditions can serve as a modest starting point for a comparative history of metaphors of visuality, and I hope I have suggested that at least some elements in Russian and Arabic philosophy are visual in a different way than the apparently "natural" visuality that is being celebrated today in the West.

For further reading

Florensky, *The Pillar and Ground of the Truth: An Essay in Orthodox Theodicy in Twelve Letters* (Princeton NJ: Princeton University Press, 1997); Florenskiy, *Анализ пространственности и времени в художественно-изобразительных произведениях (Analysis of Space and Time in Art and Pictorial Production)* (Moscow, 1993); Florenskiy, *мнимости в геометрии (The Imaginary in Geometry* (Moscow, 1922); Al-Suhrawardi, *Hikmat al-ishraq / Oeuvres philosophiques et mystiques de Shihabeddin Yahya Sohrawardi*, edited by Henry Corbin, *Bibliotheque Iranienne*, vol. 2 (Teheran and Paris: Institut Franco-Iranien–Librairie d'Amerique et d'Orient, 1952), 2-260; Vladimir Lossky, *The Mystical Theology of the Eastern Church* (London: J. Clarke, 1957); A. Smirnov, *Логика смысла: теория и ее приложение к анализу классической арабской философии и культуры.* (*Logic of Sense: Theory and its Implementation to the Analysis of Classical Arabic Philosophy and*

Culture) (Moscow: Languages of Slavic Culture, 2001); D.M. Dunlop, "Al-Farabi's Para-phrase of the Categories of Aristotle," *The Islamic Quarterly: A Review of Islamic Culture* 4 (1957): 168-83, ans also 5 (1959): 21-37; L.I. Vasilenko, L. I., "O magii i okkultizma v nasledii o. Pavla Florenskogo" (On Magic and Occultism in the Heriage of Father P. Florensky), in *Vestnik Pravoslavnogo Sviato-Tihonovskogo Gumanitarnogo universiteta* (Moscow, 2005), vyipusk 3.

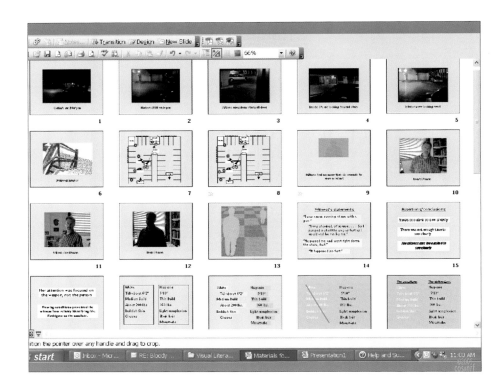

30

Teaching Visual Rhetoric to Law Students

Neal Feigenson and Christina Spiesel

Increasingly, Anglo-American legal advocates are combining images and words in computer animations, PowerPoint slide shows, and interactive CD-ROMs to present their evidence and their arguments (see also Chapter 7). To function effectively in this digital multimedia world, law students and lawyers need to develop a critical visual intelligence that enables them to anticipate the cognitive and emotional effects of word/image displays and to respond to their adversaries' presentations. They will rarely have time to research the images that they and others make, and they must be prepared to exercise their own judgment under time pressure rather than to rely on "authoritative" readings — quite different from the discipline of art history or the legal convention of arguing from precedent.

The goals of the workshop

We have several years' experience teaching visual literacy and argumentation in a one-semester course for law students, and in a considerably more condensed format to practicing lawyers. These law students and lawyers may or may not have had any prior visual training or art education. We expect that, by the end of our course, they will be able to draw on a wide range of verbal and visual materials to inform their construction of sophisticated and persuasive multimedia arguments in hypothetical (but highly realistic) cases. The teaching that is designed to get them to that point is guided by the following principles:

1. Students best learn visual literacy primarily by doing visual work (as opposed to merely being told about or shown it) and then articulating responses to what they and their classmates have done. (I.e., the learning is mainly bottom-up and experiential — which is quite nontraditional in legal education.)

2. Students best develop a reciprocally creative and disciplined approach to visual work by doing both non-case-specific (i.e., in our course, not tied to a specific legal task) and case-specific projects.

3. Students use a particular visual technology most effectively when they see it as one among many tools in a wide-ranging visual rhetorical toolkit rather than as a presentational imperative. Particular technologies come and go; a critical visual intelligence cuts across these and, following Aristotle's definition of rhetoric, chooses the one(s) most suitable to the task at hand.

4. An open and collaborative classroom setting develops future professionals' abilities to work in groups, to learn from focus groups and colleagues, and thus to refine their verbal/visual "texts" to make them more effective for their intended audiences.

The workshop

Participants in our workshops are invited as a group to use PowerPoint as a tool for thinking visually and exploring different word-image combinations. We place them in the role of attorneys representing the defendant in a simulated criminal case — an assault and robbery in a parking garage at dusk — and ask them to construct a visual argument, in the form of a PowerPoint slide show, that would be used to accompany an oral closing argument on behalf of the defendant.

The case poses issues of eyewitness identification readily understandable by non-lawyers. These include how viewing conditions in the garage (for instance poor lighting, the rapidity of the crime) may have undermined the reliability of the witness's later identification of the defendant as the perpetrator, and how the many discrepancies between the witness's initial description of the assailant to the police and the defendant's actual physical characteristics (e.g., height, weight, race) implied that the defendant could not have been the person the witness saw. We give participants a brief description of the case and their role, and then provide them with a menu of materials that they can incorporate into their visual argument, including photos, video clips, and diagrams of the crime scene, document excerpts, sample texts, and other information from the case file (photo 1). Working as a group, participants suggest elements to be incorporated into each slide; we construct the slides as they variously direct. As each new element is proposed, the group reviews and discusses the display, and thus progressively reconfigures, deletes items from, and adds more elements to the work in progress.

We organized one such workshop at the conference that was the starting point of this book; the group of participants at the conference workshop generated many ideas for visualizing the argument, engaging in a lively discussion of both the impact of individual slide designs and the pros and cons of alternative argument strategies. Some favored a paradigmatic approach, beginning with words that framed the argument as a whole (e.g., the viewing conditions argument, fol-

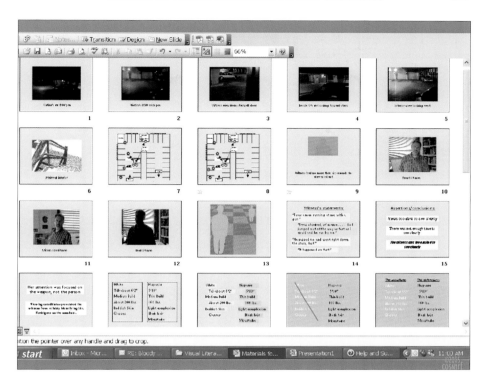

lowed by the argument based on the discrepancies) and complemented by a diagram of the crime scene that laid out the spatial relationships among perpetrator,
victim, and witness. Some, by contrast, preferred a narrative, even cinematic,
approach that immediately plunged the audience into the ill-lit garage where the
crime occurred. The group sought to accommodate the two strategies by starting
with the diagram (reproduced on the next page) and then using a video clip to
put the audience at the crime scene (a frame is shown at the bottom of the next
page). By the end of the time allotted for the workshop, however, the group was
unable to concur on a complete argument sequence.

It is instructive to compare the conference participants' (incomplete) construction with the visual arguments that emerged from two other iterations of the
workshop which we offered on other occasions. Both of these other slide sequences began with a view of the garage to launch the contention that viewing
conditions prevented any reliable identification of the perpetrator; both then
designed text, with or without images, to emphasize the discrepancies between
the witness's description of the perpetrator and the defendant's actual characteristics. Otherwise, however, the two sequences followed very different visual
logics.

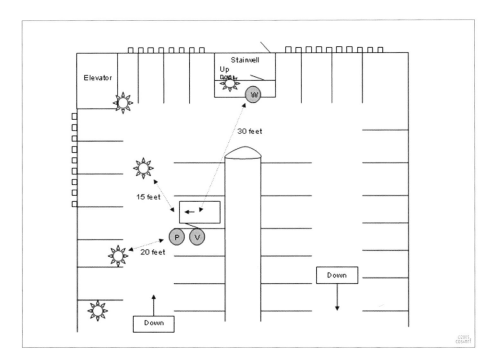

Interior view looking west

The Scene

The first sequence

The first sequence began with a still photo of the garage from the witness's point of view (above). The addition of a simple caption, "The Scene," cued the audience to anticipate a dramatic presentation — in this case, a visual closing argument conceptually located at the crime scene. The second slide presented contrasting

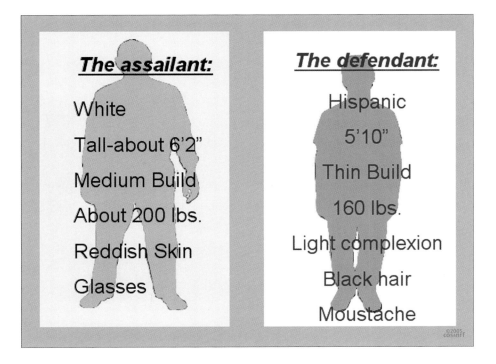

lists of the features of the assailant as the witness initially described him to the police and the defendant's actual features, as if to argue that viewing under such poor lighting conditions (as depicted in the first slide) could naturally lead to great discrepancies between an eyewitness's description of the assailant and the person whom the police happened to arrest. The simple text lists provided in the workshop materials were animated and overlaid on contrasting silhouettes of two men, underscoring the divergence between the man the witness saw at the scene and the defendant.

The third slide consisted of a pair of demonstrations: how small a figure seen at 30 feet (the initial distance between witness and perpetrator) appears compared to a figure seen at close range, and how indistinctly the facial features of a back-lit person (such as the perpetrator as seen by the witness) can be seen (shown below).

The sequence concluded by returning to the dark garage interior, this time in a video clip, on which perspectively small versions of the silhouettes of the perpetrator and the defendant were superimposed (see the illustration on the next page).

This final montage culminated a highly conceptual approach to the case that relied on visual demonstrations of arguments (e.g., the difficulty of perceiving clearly in poor lighting) rather than being confined to a strategy of simple veri-

similitude. The repetition of the iconic silhouettes — first linked to text, then to a diagram, and finally placed back in the crime scene — artfully constructed a visual through-line for the entire argument: Given that place and those conditions, a witness might readily think that she saw one man but actually have seen another, very different man.

The second sequence

The second sequence, like the first, began in the poorly lit garage, but with a video clip rather than a photo, thus immersing judge and jury in the crime scene even more vividly (top illustration on the page). This sequence then moved to the contrasting lists of physical characteristics, presented without the silhouettes or other iconic adornment (bottom of the next page). A third slide combined an animated text of the witness's initial description of the assailant with a diagram comparing the described height to the defendant's actual height, thus emphasizing both the witness's confidence in her own initial identification and the vast differences between that description and the defendant (top illustration on the page 285).

At this point this workshop group, which consisted of law professors and law students, observed a subtle rhetorical problem in the otherwise effective argument strategy so far: How to get the jury to reject the witness's identification of the defendant as the perpetrator without seeming to disparage the jury's natural tendency to identify psychologically with the victim and the witness (rather than with the perpetrator or the defendant)? In other words, the first three slides explained that poor viewing conditions can undermine eyewitness accuracy, but also posed a question: How could a presumably reasonable and clear-headed

The assailant:	**_The defendant:_**
White	Hispanic
Tall-about 6'2"	5'10"
Medium Build	Thin build
About 200 lbs.	160 lbs.
Reddish Skin	Light complexion
Glasses	Black hair
	Moustache

©2005
cosanrt

When the police came I told them the guy was a tall white male, about 6' 2", medium build – about 200 lbs, with a reddish complexion and glasses.

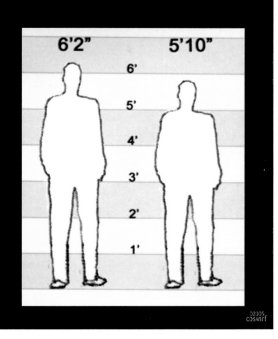

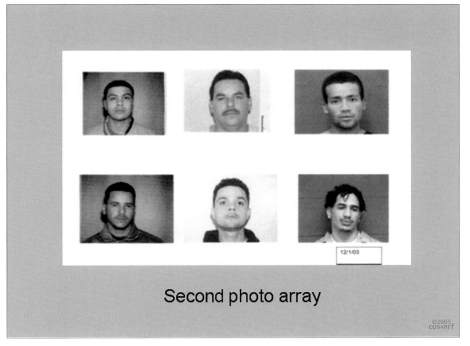

Second photo array

witness be so wrong? The group nicely resolved this dilemma with a final slide (created from additional case materials): The photo arrays that the police showed to the witness, and on the basis of which she identified the defendant as the perpetrator, were biased to elicit just that response (bottom illustration on the previous page). The entire argument sequence thus combined words and images to construct a compact problem-solution narrative — the story of a mistaken eyewitness and a falsely accused defendant — that tied together all of the defendant's major contentions in a way that would lead the jury both to decide in the defendant's favor and to feel a comfortable sense of resolution in having done so. This is the very objective of legal argument, and participants achieved it by envisioning it: They combined words and images in different ways and revised their own creations until they saw their "theory of the case" in front of them.

Outcomes

For educators in visual studies, communication studies, and other curricular areas, our interactive workshop provided three main rewards. First, it gave participants ideas for helping students to experience the fluidity with which images and words can be made to interact and the various meanings those interactions produce, an essential insight for understanding effective communication and persuasion in law or any other domain of today's visual culture. Second, the workshop modeled how teachers can flexibly deploy the resources of the most widely available presentation software in the world without being constrained by the program's too-familiar defaults. Third, we demonstrated a teaching method that began with prepared materials but did not significantly confine participants' responses to those materials; rather, the structure and the task freed participants to be inventive, to exchange their visual ideas with others, and to revise their work in light of their own and the group's shared perceptions.

Visuality in the law

The strategic uses of visual rhetoric in law is a field made possible in part by the confluence of literary theory and law, starting with Stanley Fish's work in the 1980s. One of the other books to come out of the Cork conference, *Visual Literacy,* contains an essay by Richard Sherwin, of the New York Law School, on the elaborate problems posed by such things as videos of crimes that may, or may not, be faked "art films" inspired by films such as *The Blair Witch Project.* In this book, Chapter 7 deals with the investigation of a complex incident, which is now — as the event recedes in history and memory — increasingly dependent on intricate visual reconstructions. Visual rhetoric in law is a rapidly growing field, and an excellent opportunity for fields such as literary theory, sociology, psychology, rhetoric, art, and art history, to begin a wider conversation. It is an invitation to a genuinely interdisciplionary, and preeminently *visual* conversation: and in that respect a fitting note on which to end.

For further reading:

Christopher Buccafusco, "Gaining/Losing Perspective on the Law, or Keeping Visual Evidence in Perspective," *University of Miami Law Review* 58 (2004): 609-651; *Visual Persuasion in the Skakel Trial: Enhancing Advocacy through Interactive Multimedia Presentations,* edited by Brian Carney and Neal Feigenson *Criminal Justice* 19 no. 1 (2004): 22-35; Costas Douzinas and Lynda Nead, *Law and the Image* (Chicago: University of Chicago Press, 1999); Neal Feigenson, "Digital Visual and Multimedia Software and the Reshaping of Legal Knowledge," in *Images in Law*, edited by W. Pencak and A. Wagner (London: Ashgate, c.2007); Jennifer Mnookin, "Reproducing a Trial: Evidence and its Assessment in *Paradise Lost*," in *Law on the Screen,* edited by A Sarat, L. Douglas, and M. Umphrey (Stanford, CA: Stanford University Press, 2005), 153-200; Christopher Ritter, *Creating Winning Trial Strategies and Graphics*. Chicago: American Bar Association, 2004); Christina Spiesel, "A *Las Meninas* for the Law," in *Images in Law*; and Spiesel and Feigenson, "Law in the Age of Images: The Challenge of Visual Literacy, in *Contemporary Issues of the Semiotics of Law*, edited by A. Wagner, T. Summerfield, and F. Benavides (Oxford: Hart Publishing, 2005), 231-55.

Afterword

So that ends the sample of thirty departments, thirty different ways of making and interpreting images. I will not add to the theorization I offer in the Introduction, except to say that I hope the "particulate" form of this book now makes sense. The world of visual practices is wide and deep, and if we are to understand it, we have to explore, like the first generations of linguists did, and learn to speak some of the languages used outside the enclave of the humanities.

It may surprise some North American and other English-language readers that this book is published by Wilhelm Fink. Among North American scholars, the normal protocol is to try to publish with a North American university press. If I were a younger scholar, and this was my first book, I would not have published it outside the US, and even within the US I would have tried to publish with one of the very small number of "top" academic presses interested in the history of art and science: University of California, Yale, Princeton, Cornell, Harvard, MIT, Johns Hopkins, Penn State Press, or the University of Chicago. For some scholars I know, that list is even shorter. If they can't place their books with one of those presses, they may wait for opportunities to place chapters in the equally small number of major journals, or in specialized anthologies. The only alternatives to the short list of US presses are normally Cambridge, Oxford, Routledge UK, Yale (London), and perhaps Reaktion. A North American scholar working with French materials might also seek to co-publish her book with Minuit, Flammarion, Gallimard, or another French publisher. A North American scholar working on a German subject might try to find a publisher in Germany. But even in those cases, the books would be co-published (for example, by Flammarion and Yale University Press); and in fact very few English-speaking scholars in the humanities try to co-publish on the Continent. This book is doubly unusual, therefore, because it is not being co-published in the United States.

The reasons are somewhat delicate, but worth exploring. First it needs to be said that English speakers often read only in English. Some European publishers are not considered serious even if they publish in English, and even if they are based in England. Ashgate, Palgrave, and Sage, for example, are popular among scholars in the UK, but they might be considered second-tier choices by scholars in the US. A North American art historian, seeing a book published by Ashgate or Palgrave, might well assume that the manuscript had been rejected by North American presses. (That notion is, in my experience, wholly confined to North America, and no such stigma attaches to Ashgate or Palgrave in the UK.) This cultural prejudice and scholarly isolationism means that even excellent German presses such as Wilhelm Fink, Wagenbach, Suhrkamp, and Riemer are virtually invisible, and largely unknown, in North America. (And so are newer presses such as Turia und Kant and Diaphanes, which are very roughly like Macula in

France and Reaktion in the UK: that is, they might be inadvisable choices for young scholars in the US who need a major press for their first publication.[1]) Because they generally do not sell many books, German academic publishers do not advertise widely, retain aggressive international distributors, or attend book fairs. As a result, German academic publishers are not well represented in North American academic conferences or university bookstores. (That non-participation is also due to the different ethos of academic publishing in Germany, which is less commercially oriented than in the US. This book is has a very small print run and is subsidized in order to keep the retail price at a reasonable level. However, the subsidy alone would put it out of reach of most young scholars in the US or UK who were looking to publish their first book.[2]) Those few Continental presses that are known in the US, Australia, and the UK — Prestel, for example, which has offices in New York — are considered to be less scholarly.

North American scholars intent on their careers, who need to be taken seriously among their academic colleagues, generally avoid presses other than the University of California, Yale, Princeton, Cornell, and the others I've mentioned; and books published by any other presses — and especially those on the Continent — will be looked on skeptically, as if they are either irrelevant or second-rate because their authors had failed to publish with a first-rank US publisher.

Why, then publish this book with Wilhelm Fink? For three reasons.

1. Most research on science and non-art images is done in German-speaking countries and in Scandinavia. The word *Bildwissenschaft* has recently been revived, by Horst Bredekamp and others, to describe an historical approach to the study of images that stresses non-art and technical images.[3] (In English-language scholarship, *Bildwissenchaft* has recently been given an entirely different valence.[4]) Images outside of art have been theorized by a number of German, Austrian, and Swiss scholars including Joël Sakarovitch, Wolfgang Pircher, Karin Leonhard, and especially Peter Geimer.[5] In Basel, Gottfried Boehm and others have initiated a project called Eikones, which also aims at an inclusive study of all images.[6] In Scandinavia a similarly inflected study of non-art images is called "visual studies," and it goes by other names as well — "iconic criticism," "image studies," "image science."[7] It's pertinent, also, that the "iconic turn" in German scholarship (associated with Boehm, who coined the expression in 1994) is different from the "pictorial turn" in English-language scholarship (associated with W.J.T. Mitchell, who coined it in 1992).[8]

The names do not matter as much as what is studied. Visual studies in English-speaking countries, and in places influenced by them, is restricted much more tightly to fine art and popular art. There are several emergent differences between scholarship inspired or informed by the "iconic turn" and scholarship informed by the "pictorial turn," among them the wider sense of *Bild* in German, as opposed to English *picture;* but in effect, the German literature of the last ten years has been significantly more involved with the particulars of "epistemic" or "tech-

[handwritten margin note: difference between pictorial turn + iconic turn]

nical" images outside of art. As I mentioned in the Introduction, this book was originally to have been published along with the proceedings of a conference called "Visual Literacy." The conference proceedings, which will appear as two separate books — *Visual Cultures* and *Visual Literacy* — reflect the state of visual studies in mainly Anglophone countries. Despite the wide range of papers, there is virtually no science in those two books. (The principal exception is an essay by Matthias Bruhn and Vera Dünkel, members of the unit called "Das Technische Bild" at the Humboldt-Universität in Berlin.[9]) The near-absence of non-art images from the two other conference books is not happenstance, but structural: the number of scholars in North America and the UK who study non-art images is very small. One might name Lisa Cartwright among visual studies scholars, and there are Martin Kemp, Linda Dalrymple Henderson, John Gage, and a half-dozen others in art history. Journals like the *Journal of Visual Culture* are uniformly uninterested in image-making outside of mass culture and fine art.

This book, therefore, is partly a response to visual studies as it is known in Anglophone countries. I am concerned that the field restricts itself too much to images in popular culture and fine art. The wider world of image-making practices is usually only acknowledged by pointing to the social construction of science — its entanglement in politics, gender, identity, and the society that provides its institutional structures. What is missing in that approach is really nothing less than the visual languages of science and other non-art practices. This book is meant as a sampler of the kinds of complexity that inhere in visual practices when they are considered in detail. Hence the first reason for publishing with Wilhelm Fink: Germany is in the part of the world where visual studies has the best chance of becoming the broad-based, university-wide field that it should be.

2. There is a custom in publishing in the humanities, according to which books should be continuous narratives, uninterrupted by problem sets, equations, and graphs. In the long-standing tradition of humanist scholarship, such books are for the "general reader"; they are intended to be non-technical even if they involve special lexica and jargon. I sent this book, in manuscript, to two prominent university presses in North America, before I decided a German press is more appropriate. In both of the US presses, the Acquisitions Editors rejected the manuscript on the grounds that it was too technical. As I mentioned in the Introduction, one editor said it was too "particulate," by which she meant not sufficiently woven into a single continuous narrative. (She recommended I write the thirty chapters into a single text on the model of the Introduction.) As I argued in the Introduction, it is wholly appropriate and deliberate that this book is partly fragmentary, "particulate," and technical. Those qualities are meant as responses to the uniformly non-technical, undetailed exposition of non-art images in more Anglophone scholarship.

3. In the US and other countries, some university presses are inclined away from elementary pedagogy. They see it as their purpose to produce professional-level research and books that drive disciplines forward. Textbooks are mainly thought to be the domain of specialized publishers. One of the US editors who saw this book in manuscript thought it might make a good first-year textbook, but felt that the pedagogic purpose made it unsuitable for a university press. Of course there are exceptions to this rule (many university presses in the US also publish textbooks) but for the most part, textbooks are handled by non-university, "trade" publishers. This book is again a special case. I would be glad if it were used as a textbook: I used a working version of it to teach this material in Ireland, to first-year undergraduates, with some of the authors as guest speakers. It is certainly amenable to that approach. But it is also intended as an experiment, a way of pushing a little on the field of visual studies to see what it might look like if it takes first-year education seriously. For that reason I thought an academic publisher would be appropriate.

Those are the reasons this book was published in Germany. I hope that this gesture suggests that visual studies should be as international as possible. The kinds of visual studies practiced in the US, Canada, Australia, New Zealand, and the UK (and in countries influenced by them) can learn a lot from the highly detailed, technophilic visual studies practiced in German-speaking countries and in Scandinavia. The opposite is also true: the emphasis on politics and identity that are the cornerstones of English-language scholarship have already had interesting effects on German-language writing. There are also ways of practicing visual culture beyond the ones I have mentioned. There is a kind of visual studies in South America that comes in part from communications theory and semiotics, and a kind in the People's Republic of China that intersects with aesthetics and cultural heritage. By publishing this book in Germany, I hope to suggest that the conversation on visual studies can be broader and more challenging than it sometimes has been.

It seems to me that restricting visual studies to art and popular culture risks missing a tremendous opportunity. Visual studies can become the place where images and visuality are studied for the entire university, and not just for the humanities. To do that, it is necessary to spend time considering unfamiliar visual practices *in detail*, and not as examples of other practices to which they may not be directly related.

Notes to Afterword

1 I thank Wolfram Pichler for pointing me to Turia und Kant and Diaphanes.

2 This book has a print run of 500, augmented with 100 personal copies for distribution. A typical visual culture or science studies book in the US would have a print run of 2,000 to 3,000, approximately 280 copies of which go to the principal university libraries in the US and UK.

3 See first Bredekamp and Pablo Schneider, "Visuelle Argumentationen — Die Mysterien der Repräsentation und die Berechenbarkeit der Welt," in the book of the same title, edited by Brekedamp and Schneider (Munich: Wilhelm Fink, 2006), 7-10; and for an excellent example of the confluence of technical and historical analysis of images, see his *Darwins Korallen: Due frühen Evolutionsdiagramme und die Tradition der Naturgeschichte* (Berlin: Klaus Wagenbach, 2005). Bredekamp's argument about *Bildwissenschaft* was made for an English-language readership in "A Neglected Tradition? Art History as *Bildwissenschaft*," *Critical Inquiry* 29 no. 3 (2003): 418-29. See further *Bildwissenschaft: Disziplinen, Themen, Methoden,* edited by Klaus Sachs-Hombach (Frankfurt a.M.: Suhrkamp, 2005); and the review by Carolin Behrmann and Jan von Brevern, in *ArtHist: Netzwerk für Kunstgeschichte im H-net,* 9 November 2005, www.arthist.net/DocBookD. html, November 2006, which has an interesting summary of aproaches to pictures.

4 The word *Bildwissenschaft* was appropriated by W.J.T. Mitchell in a talk given at the conference that originally was to be published along with the material in this book. In *Visual Literacy* (New York: Routledge, 2007), Mitchell uses the word to describe some fundamental properties of visual interpretation. It is a newly-minted sense, however, not meant to be connected to the German usage.

5 I thank Wolfram Pichler for bringing my attention to Sakarovitch and Pircher. See Sakarovitch, *Epures d'architecture: de la coupe des pierres à la géométrie descriptive XVIe-XIXe siècles* (Basel: Birkhäuser, 1998*); Kunst, Zeichen, Technik: Philosophie am Grund der Medien,* edited by Marianne Kubaczek and Wolfgang Pircher (Münster: LIT, 2004); *Ordnungen der Sichtbarkeit: Fotografie in Wissenschaft, Kunst und Technologie* (Frankfurt a. M.: Suhrkamp, 2002); *Was ist ein Bild?,* edited by Gottfried Boehm (Munich: Wilhelm Fink, 1994). For Leonhard see for example "Was ist Raum im 17. Jahrhunderts? Die Raumfrage des Barocks: Von Descartes zu Newton und Leibniz," in *Visuelle Argumentationen: Die Mysterien der Repräsentation und die Berechenbarkeit der Welt,* edited by Horst Brekedamp and Pablo Schneider (Munich: Wilhelm Fink, 2006), 11-34; and Leonhard, *Das gemalte Zimmer: Zur Interieurmalerei Jan Vermeers* (Munich: Wilhelm Fink, 2003).

6 Eikones (National Centres of Competence in Research [NCCR] "Bildkritik" or "Iconic Criticism") is a Swiss National Science Foundation project, which began in October 2005. As of autumn 2006, it was divided into six modules, studying different aspects of the image including images in literature, architecture, anthropology, science, and engineering. The modules were organized according to a range of conceptual frameworks: iconophilia and iconoclasm, the "power of images," the generation of meaning, image politics, visualization, the epistemic image (principally scientific images), memory, aporetic images, and a number of others. As of this writing (March 2007) the project is in early stages, and most of the material is unpublished aside from NCCR publicity materials, which are partly on the website, www.eikones.ch.

7 For references see my *Visual Studies: A Skeptical Introduction* (New York: Routledge, 2003), chapter 1.

8 In the German literature, see *Iconic Turn: Die neue Macht der Bilder,* edited by Hubert Burda and Christa Maar (Cologne: DuMont Literatur und Kunst, 2004), and the review by Carlin Behrmann and Jan von Brevern, in *ArtHist: Netzwerk für Kunstgeschichte im H-net,* 2 November 2005, www. arthist.net/DocBookD.html, November 2006. In addition to sources cited above, see *Logik der Bilder: Präsenz — Repräsentation — Erkenntnis,* edited by Richard Hoppe-Sailer, Claus Volkenandt and Gundolf Winter (Berlin: Reimer, 2005), especially the introduction "Logik der Bilder," pp. 9-16.

9 The essay is in the book *Visual Literacy* (New York: Routledge, 2007).

Contributors

Francis Burke is Senior Lecturer/Consultant and Head, Department of Restorative Dentistry, The University Dental School and Hospital, Cork. His main interests are teaching operative dentistry and oral care for the elderly. His publications include "Progressive Changes in the Pulpo-Dentinal Complex and Their Clinical Consequences," *Gerodontology* 12 no. 2 (December 1995): 57-66. He is currently the President of the British Society of Gerodontology (2005) and Past-President (2000-2002) of the Irish Division, International Association for Dental Research. (Department of Restorative Dentistry, University Dental School and Hospital, Wilton Cork, f.burke@ucc.ie)

Paul Callanan teaches Physics and Astronomy in the Department of Physics at University College, Cork. His research concerns the study of very compact stars —including black holes — in our Galaxy, across the range of the electromagnetic spectrum. He has used many of the world's largest telescopes to this end, and very much agrees with Einstein that "the most incomprehensible thing about the universe is that it is comprehensible."

John Carey is a lecturer in the Department of Early and Medieval Irish, University College Cork. His publications include the books *King of Mysteries: Early Irish Religious Writings* (Dublin, 1998) and *A Single Ray of the Sun: Religious Speculation in Early Ireland* (Andover & Aberystwyth, 1999). He is preparing a study of color taxonomy and color symbolism, as these are reflected in certain Old Irish texts. (j.carey@ucc.ie.)

John Considine lectures in the Department of Economics, University College, Cork. His publications include "Constitutional Interpretation: Edmund Burke and James Buchanan and their 18th Century Intellectual Roots," *Constitutional Political Economy* 17 (2006): 71-85; "The Simpsons: Public Choice in the Tradition of Swift and Orwell," *Journal of Economic Education* 7 no. 2 (2006): 17-228; and (with Seamus Coffey and Daniel Kiely) "Irish Sports Capital Funding: A Public Choice Perspective," *European Sports Management Quarterly* 4 no. 3 (2004): 150-69.

James Elkins teaches at the School of the Art Institute of Chicago, and is Manager of Events and Publications at University College Cork, Ireland. His most recent books include *Visual Studies: A Skeptical Introduction* (New York, 2003), *On The Strange Place of Religion in Contemporary Art* (New York, 2004), *Master Narratives and Their Discontents* (New York, 2005), and the edited volumes

Photography Theory and *Is Art History Global?* (New York, 2006). (mail@imagehistory.org)

Neal Feigenson is Professor of Law at Quinnipiac University School of Law and Research Affiliate in the Yale University Department of Psychology. He is the author of *Legal Blame: How Jurors Think and Talk about Accidents* (Washington, DC, 2000). Other recent publications include "Emotions and Attributions of Legal Responsibility and Blame: A Research Review" (with Jaihyun Park), *Law and Human Behavior* 30 (2006): 143-161; "Too Real? The Future of Virtual Reality Evidence," *Law and Policy*, 28 (2006): 271-293; and "Law in the Age of Images: The Challenge of Visual Literacy" (with Christina Spiesel and Richard Sherwin), *in Contemporary Issues of the Semiotics of Law,* edited by Anne Wagner, Tracy Summerfield, and Farid Benavides (Oxford, 2005), 231-255. (275 Mt. Carmel Avenue, Hamden, CT 06518; feigenson@quinnipiac.edu)

Paul Fletcher is Professor of Speech and Hearing Sciences at University College Cork. He held previous academic appointments at the Universities of Reading and Hong Kong. His research interests are in language development and language imapirment in children; he has published widely on these topics in relation to children learning English and Chinese. Among his book-length publications are *A Child's Learning of English* (1986), *Language Acquisition*, edited with Michael Garman (1989); and *Developmental Theory and Language Disorders,* edited with Jon Miller (2005).

Robert Fourie lectures in the Department of Speech and Hearing Sciences at University College Cork. He has worked variously as an audiological scientist and speech and language therapist for deaf children. His publications include "Frequency Specificity and Oto-Acoustic Emissions" (Johannesburg, 1992), 19-21; "Efficiency Of A Hearing Person Learning Sign Language Vocabulary From Media versus A Teacher" (East Yorkshire, 2002), 45-60; and "Language Planning Issues in the Education of Deaf Children" (Dublin, 2005), 96-108.

Catherine Gorman works at the Department of Restorative Dentistry at University College Cork. She lectures in dental technology to both undergraduate and postgraduate students. Her publications include "The Influence of Some Different Factors on the Accuracy of Shade Selection," *Journal of Oral Rehabilitation* 31 no. 9 (2004): 900-4; "Heat-Pressed Ionomer Glass-Ceramics, Part I: An Investigation of the Flow and Microstructure," *Dental Materials* 19 (2003): 320-26; and Part II *Ibid.* 20 (2004) 252-61.

Bettie Higgs is a lecturer in the Department of Geology at University College Cork, Ireland. Her areas of interest include plate tectonics and the use of geophysics to investigate the subsurface. In addition she tutors geology to non-traditional students in the Centre for Adult and Continuing Education, and the Open University. She is interested in the public understanding of science, and coordinates activities designed to support staff in their teaching and learning role in UCC. (b.higgs@ucc.ie)

Eithne Hunt lectures in the Department of Occupational Therapy, University College Cork. Her teaching and research interests centre on the relationship between daily occupations and health and well-being. She would like to aknowledge the session facilitators — Colette Lewis, Cork Artists Collective, Catherine Phillips, the Crawford College of Art and Design, and the team at Cork Printmakers.

Hugh Kavanagh is an Architectural Technician and Surveyor. He graduated as an Architectural Technician from Waterford I.T in 1995 before working with Ben Murtagh on conservation works at Reginald's Tower, Waterford city and at Kilkenny Castle; in 1999 he joined Valerie J. Keeley Ltd. as an AutoCAD Technician, working on large infrastuctural works such as the N9 Dublin to Waterford motorway and Carrickmines Castle, Dublin. He has worked with the Archaeological Services Unit at the University college Cork since 2003. His publications include graphic work for Excavations in Cork 1984-2000; the Keiller Knowles Collection by Peter Woodman; and a number of articles for the *Journal of the Cork Historical and Archaeological Society.* He has designed graphics and presentations for the European Association of Archaeologists, Cork County Council and UCC. He is an associate member of the Association of Archaeological Illustrators and Surveyors.

Sabine Kriebel is a Lecturer in History of Art at the University College Cork. Before coming to Ireland, she worked at the National Gallery of Art, Washington, DC, in a postdoctoral capacity where she collaborated on a major exhibition of Dada and assisted in the Department of Photographs. She is currently writing a book on the 1930s photomontages of John Heartfield. Her publications include "Theorizing Photography: A Short History," the Introduction to *Photography Theory*, edited by James Elkins (New York: Routledge, 2006); "Die Gestaltung der Ruine: Caspar Walter Rauh und die Nachkriegszeit," in *Caspar Walter Rauh: Schwierige Verzauberung,* exhibition catalogue, (Bauman Verlag, 2005); and "What is Dada and What Does it Want in Cologne?" in *Dada: Zurich, Berlin, Hannover, Cologne, New York, Paris,* edited by Leah Dickerman (New York: Distributed Art Publishers, 2005).

Pierre Laszlo is a French science writer and Professor of Chemistry emeritus at the University of Liège (Belgium) as well as the École polytechnique (Palaiseau,

France), with earlier positions at Princeton University and the Université d'Orsay and visiting professorships at the Universities of Connecticut, Kansas, California (Berkeley), Chicago, Colorado, Johns Hopkins, Lausanne, Hamburg, Toulouse and Cornell. He has written a dozen books to communicate chemical science to the general public, for which he received in 1999 the Maurice Pérouse Prize from the Fondation de France and in 2004 the Paul Doistau-Blutet Prize from the French Academy of Sciences. His latest books are *Le Phénix et la salamandre* (Le Pommier, Paris, 2004), *NO*, a pedagogic wordplay written jointly with Carl Djerassi (Deutscher Theaterverlag, Weinheim, 2003), *Qu'est-ce que l'alchimie?* (Paris: Hachette Littératures-Pluriel, 2003), *Les odeurs nous parlent-elles?* (Paris: Le Pommier, 2003), *L'architecture du vivant* (Paris: Flammarion, 2002), *Pourquoi la mer est-elle bleue?* and *Peut-on boire l'eau du robinet?* (Paris: Le Pommier, 2002), *Salt: Grain of Life* (New York: HarperCollins, 2002). Laszlo and his wife, the graphic artist Valerie Annette Jann, live in Sénergues, France and in Pinehurst, North Carolina, USA.

Nuala Lordan, see **Mary Wilson**

Ivor MacCarthy is a Senior Lecturer at the Department of Geology at University College Cork, Ireland. His research interests are concerned with the reconstruction of past environments through studies of ancient sediments. His work is focused on Devonian-Carboniferous sedimentary rocks and Pleistocene fluvio-glacial and marine sediments in Ireland. This work has resulted in the production of a number of geological maps, which depict the geological structure and composition of parts of southern Ireland. Some of this work has been carried out in conjunction with the Geological Survey of Ireland. While the maps are important data sources, they also interpret the geological structure and environmental aspects of the rock record.

Brendan McElroy is a lecturer in the Department of Economics, University College Cork. He got his PhD from University of Edinburgh in health economics. His recent publications include Virginia Wiseman, Brendan McElroy, Lesong Conteh et al., "Malaria Prevention in The Gambia: Patterns of Expenditure and Determinants of Demand at the Household Level," *Tropical Medicine and International Health* 11 (2006): 419-31; and Ann Kirby and Brendan McElroy, "Does Attendance Affect Grade? An Analysis of First Year Economics Students in Ireland," *Economic and Social Review* 34 no 3 (2003): 311–26.

David O'Byrne works at the Department of Computer Science at University College Cork, Ireland.

Jim McGrath studies at the Department of Civil and Environmental Engineering at University College Cork where he is pursuing a PhD in the area of "Advanced Signal and Image Processing Techniques for Automated Mapping" under the joint supervision of J. Philip O'Kane and Richard C. Kavanagh. He is a graduate of the Department of Electrical and Electronic Engineering. (j.k.mcgrath@student.ucc.ie)

Stephen Mc Grath works with Douwe van Sinderen at the Department of Microbiology at University College Cork. His research focuses on the molecular biology of bacteriophages and his publications include "Anatomy of a bacteriophage tail" *Journal of Bacteriology* 188, pp. 3972-3982; and "Identification and Characterization of Phage-Resistance Genes in Temperate Lactococcal bacteriophages," *Molecular Microbiology* 43, pp. 509-20.

Paul McSweeney is Senior Lecturer in the Department of Food and Nutritional Sciences at University College Cork, Ireland. and has a BSc in Food Science and Technology and a PhD in Food Chemistry from the same university. The overall theme of his research is dairy biochemistry with particular reference to factors affecting cheese flavour. He is co-author or co-editor of 6 books and about 150 research papers and reviews. He was awarded the Marschall Danisco International Dairy Science Award in 2004.

Pat Meere is a lecturer in the Department of Geology at University College Cork, Ireland. His recent publications include: Meere and Kevin Mulchrone, "Timing of Deformation within Old Red Sandstone Lithologies from the Dingle Peninsula, SW Ireland," *Journal of the Geological Society* 163: 461-469; Meere, K.R. Choudhury, and Kevin Mulchrone, *Journal of Structural Geology* 28 no. 3: 363-375; and Meere, D. Quinn, and J.A. Wartho, "A Chronology of Foreland Deformation: Ultra-Violet Laser Ar^{40}/Ar^{39} Dating of Syn/late-Orogenic Intrusions from the Variscides of Southwest Ireland," *Journal of Structural Geology* 27 no. 8: 1413-1425.

Kieran Mulchrone works at the Department of Applied Mathematics at University College, Cork where he teaches modeling and numerical computing. His research is at the interface of structural geology and applied mathematics and is concerned with understanding the behavior of rocks during deformation. He has published over 20 scientific papers in the *Journal of Structural Geology, Tectonophysics*, and *Computers and Geosciences* (k.mulchrone@ucc.ie).

Caitríona Ó Dochartaigh works at the Department of Early and Medieval Irish, University College Cork. Her publications include "Questions of Orality, Performance and Transmission in Relation to Early Irish Prayer," *in Festgabe für*

Hildegard L.C. Tristram zum sechzigsten Gebürtstag, edited by G. Hemprich et al. (Freiburg, 2001), 215-22; "Language and Identity in Early Medieval Ireland," *Études Irlandaises* 27 no. 2 (2002), 119-31; "Goethe's Translation from the Gaelic Ossian," in *The Reception of Ossian, European Critical Traditions: The Reception of British Authors in Europe,* edited H. Gaskill, (London, 2004), 156-75. (Dept of Early and Medieval Irish, UCC, Cork)

Nollaig Parfrey is professor of Pathology and consultant histopathologist at University College Cork and Cork University Hospital, Ireland. A medical graduate of University College Cork, his postgraduate training was at Johns Hopkins Hospital, USA and at McGill University, Canada. His research interests are in human molecular genetics, primarily in mapping and identifying human disease genes.

Marc Shorten works and studies at the Department of Zoology, Ecology and Plant Science at University College, Cork. His publications include Dorothy Cross, Tom Cross, and Marc Shorten, "Medusae," in *Experiment: Conversations in Art and Science,* edited by B. Arends and D. Thackara (London: The Wellcome Trust, 2003), 16-61; and Shorten, John Davenport, J.E. Seymour, M. Cross, T.J. Carrette, G. Woodward, and Tom Cross, "Kinematic analysis of Swimming in Australian Box Jellyfish, *Chiropsalmus sp* and *Chironex fleckeri* (Cubozoa, Cnidaria: Chirodropidae)," Journal of Zoology (London) 267 no. 4 (2005): 371-380.

Christina Spiesel is an artist and writer who is an Adjunct Professor of Law at both Quinnipiac University School of Law and New York Law School, and a Senior Research Scholar at the Yale Law School. Spiesel has been exhibiting her art since 1972. Her published writing includes: "A *Las Meniñas* for the Law," *in Images in Law* (Hampshire, UK, 2006); "Law in the Digital Age: How Visual Communication Technologies are Transforming the Practice, Theory, and Teaching of Law" (with Richard Sherwin and Neal Feigenson), Boston *University Journal of Science and Technology Law*, 2006; and "Law in the Age of Images" (also with Sherwin and Feigenson), in *Contemporary Issues of the Semiotics of Law* (London, 2005). Publication on arts issues include "Female Trouble" *in Trickster and Duality: The Dance of Differentiation,* edited by C.W. Spinks. A digital video, *Dream,* can be seen at www.poppingpixels.org. She was a contributor to SIGGRAPH 2006.

Bernadette Sweeney lectures in Drama and Theatre Studies at University College Cork. She directed theatre productions including Euripides's "Helen" (2004), a devised piece "wordmadeflesh" (2004), and a collaboration with half/angel dance theatre company on "The White Quadrangle" (2005). Her published articles and chapters include *"wordmadeflesh*: Writing the Body in Irish Theatre," in *Modern Drama,* edited by Brian Singleton and Karen Fricker (Toronto: University of Toronto Press, 2004); a biographical entry on Tom Mac Intyre *in Dictionary of Literary Biography 245: British and Irish Dramatists since WWII, Third Series,* edited by John Bull (Bruccoli Clark Layman, Inc., 2001); and "Form and Comedy in Contemporary Irish Theatre," in *The Power of Laughter,* edited by Eric Weitz (Dublin: Carysfort Press, 2004). She is developing a project on Irish Live Art with her colleague Franc Chamberlain. (b.sweeney@ucc.ie)

Andy Wheeler is a College Lecturer and Earth Science Degree Co-ordinator at the Department of Geology, University College Cork, Ireland. He has published extensively in national and international scientific journals and books on aspects of marine geology, from the sedimentary signature of storms and the environmental controls on shipwreck preservations, to the functioning of deep-water coral reefs. Selected recent publications can be found at www.ucc.ie/academic/geology/people/staff/ajw.html. (a.wheeler@ucc.ie)

Darius Whelan is a lecturer at the Faculty of Law, University College Cork, where he teaches Employment Law, Internet Regulation and International Trade Law. His publications and papers have covered topics such as criminal insanity law, mental health tribunals, use of the internet by lawyers and freedom of information law. He also runs the Irish Law site (www.irishlaw.org) and Irish Law discussion list. (d.whelan@ucc.ie)

Mary Wilson, **Nuala Lordan** and **Deirdre Quirke** are all members of the Department of Applied Social Studies at University College Cork. Their joint publications include "When Words Are Not Enough: 'Facilitating angels in the funzone!'" in *Social Work with Groups,* edited by Carol Kuechler (New York, 2005); "Funzone: Using Groupwork for Teaching and learning," in *Groupwork*, edited by Mark Doel (London 2004), 9-29; "Family, Community, Church, and State: Natural Parents Talking about Adoption in Ireland," *British Journal of Social Work* 34 (2004): 621-48; "Maskmaking and Social Groupwork," in *Social Work with Groups*, edited by Carol Cohen (New York, 2003); "Breaking the Mold: Maskmaking as in Inclusive Educational Tool," in *Life's Rich Pattern: Cultural Diversity and the Education of Adults,* edited by David Jones and Gerald Normie (Glasgow 2002), 152-67.

Gerard Wrixon was President of University College Cork at the time this book went to press, and his generous support of the History of Art Department made the entire exhibition, conference, and publications (both this book and *Visual Literacy* and *Visual Cultures,* the companion volumes) possible.

Anna Zenkova, PhD, is working for a postdoctoral degree at the Institute of Philosophy and Law of the Urals Division of the Russian Academy of Sciences, Yekaterinburg, Russia. Her publications include "Visual Metaphor in Social and Political Discourse: Methodological Aspects," "Meaning Construction Mechanisms in Western and Arabic Cultures," "Death of the Animated Cartoon Character," "Visual Studies as Integral Part of Social and Humanitarian Knowledge," "Critique of Ocularcentrism in Modern Western Philosophy," and "The Construction Problem of a New Ontology of Vision in Maurice Merleau-Ponty's Philosophy" (all in Russian). (azenkova@gmail.com)

Photo credits and acknowledgments

All photos are original with the authors or in the public domain, with the following exceptions:

Introduction:
Moss-covered tree: From Smock, "Picture This!" in *California Monthly* (March/April 2005), pp. 16-27. Courtesy Kerry Tremain, Editor, *California Monthly* (kerry@alumni.berkeley.edu)
Hybrid Medical Animation still: www.hybridmedicalanimation.com; contact info@hybridmedicalanimation.com
Atoms "dancing": see http://domino.watson.ibm.com/comm/pr.nsf/pages/rsc.sub-a.html
Bernd Thaller's animation: bernd.thaller@uni-graz.at
Hungarian film of AFM: www.mfa.kfki.hu/int/nano/online/kirchberg2001/; animation courtesy Daróczi, Csaba Sándor, daroczi@mfa.kfki.hu, and Geza Mark, mark@mfa.kfki.hu
Copper animation: www.llnl.gov/largevis/atoms/ductile-failure/index.html; animation by Farid Abraham, abraham4@llnl.gov
Ribbon diagram of molecule: courtesy Pierre Kennepohl, pierre@chem.ubc.ca
Ball model of molecule: courtesy University of Texas at Austin, Rand Martin, rand@ices.utexas.edu; www.ticam.utexas.edu/CCV/gallery/molecular-images/
Head of virus: courtesy Steven McQuinn, steven_mcq@yahoo.com
Soil atlas: University of Nebraska Press, thanks to Elaine Maruhn, emaruhn1@unl.edu
Biotic communities atlas: courtesy University of Utah Press
Citrus atlas: courtesy Directeur de l'Information, OCDE, 2, rue André-Pascal, 75775 Paris DECEX 16

Chapter 2:
Thanks to Half/Angel dance theatre company, DTS student performers, er FitzGibbon, Bryan Ferriter, and the Glucksman Gallery.

Chapter 4:
Cover of *Constitutional Political Economy,* spring/summer 1991: courtesy the Editor, Alan Hamln; the Center for Study of Public Choice, George Mason University; and Springer Verlag, permissions.dordrecht@springer.com

Chapter 5:
Book of Ballymote, MS 23 P 12, f. 170v and f. 168v: courtesy the Royal Irish Academy, Dublin; www.isos.dias.ie; thanks to Siobhan Fitzpatrick and Petra Schnabel, s.fitzpatrick@ria.ie, P.Schnabel@ria.ie.

Chapter 7:
Courtesy of Nell McCafferty and Denis Bradley, Bloody Sunday Tribunal, Northern Ireland Council for Curriculum Examination and Assessment. Acknowledgments are also due to the Virtual Reality System Team at Northern Ireland Centre for Learning Resources: Derek Kinnen, Company Director; Malachy McDaid, Senior Designer; Rosemary Gordon, Photographer; Marc Harewood, Architect's Technician responsible for 3D modelling.

Chapter 8:
Photo 8 is courtesy Hal Burch and Bill Cheswick, research.lumeta.com/ches/map/; ches@lumeta.com
Photos 9, 10, and 11: courtesy Lisa Jevbratt, jevbratt.com/1_to_1/, jevbratt@jevbratt.com. Photos 9 and 10: *Migration: Interface 1*, 2005. Photo 11: *1:1 Interface: Every IP*, 1999-2002.

Chapter 9:
Sincere thanks to the session facilitators, Colette Lewis, Cork Artists Collective (Photography); Catherine Phillips, Crawford College of Art & Design (Art) and the team at Cork Printmakers (Printmaking); and all who contributed to the experience.

Chapter 12:
Photos 1 and 2: courtesy Gerard Wrixon
Photo 2 is from Chrisopher Martin et al., "The AST/RO Survey of the Galactic Center Region. I. The Inner 3 Degrees," *ApJS* 150 (2004): 239, plate 6; courtesy Christopher Martin, Chris.Martin@oberlin.edu
Photo 3 is from Tsuyoshi Sawada et al., "A Molecular Face-on View of the Galactic Centre Region," arXiv:astro-ph/0401286 v1 15 Jan 2004, Fig. 11; courtesy Tsuyoshi Sawada, sawada@nro.nao.ac.jp. The essay was published in *Monthly Notices of the Royal Astronomical Society* 349 (2004): 1167-1178.
Photo 4 is from Farhad Yusef-Zadeh et al., "Starburst Driven Thermal and Nonthermal Structures in the Galactic Center Region," Fig. 1, courtesy Farhad Yusef-Zadeh, zadeh@northwestern.edu
Photos 5 and 6 are from T. Ott et al., "Inward Bound: Studying The Galactic Center With Naos/Conica," figs. 1 and 4. Courtesy Reinhard Genzel, genzel@mpe.mpg.de

Chapter 13:
Image of the Cork Waterworks: courtesy Colin Rynne
Bronze Age pots and house: courtesy Rhoda Cronin

Chapter 15:
Book of Kells *chi-rho* page: courtesy Trinity College, Dublin.

Chapter 17:
Acknowledgments to Douwe van Sinderen, Alimentary Pharmabiotic Centre, University College Cork; and the Science Foundation Ireland. Photographs of phages courtesy Horst Neve, Institute for Microbiology, Federal Research Centre for Nutrition and Food, Kiel.

Chapter 18:
Acknowledgments to Tom Cross, John Davenport and Tom Kelly.

Chapter 27:
Stephen McGrath acknowledges the financial support of Science Foundation Ireland.

Chapter 29:
The editor would like to thank Clemena Antonova for a critical reading of the chapter, and for suggesting Vasilenko's text.

Chapter 30:
The authors would like to acknowledge James McKay and Catherine Meyer, Connecticut (USA) Division of Public Defender Services, Training Department for their contribution of materials, Deans Brad Saxton of Quinnipiac University School of Law and Harold Koh of Yale Law School for their support of this research; and Anne Higonnet for her ideas in one of our workshops.